D1590187

EDITORIAL ADVISORY BOARD

Myron G. Eisenberg, Ph.D., is Chief of the Psychology Service at the Department of Veterans Affairs Medical Center in Hampton, Virginia and is Associate Professor of Physical Medicine and Rehabilitation and Psychiatry and Behavioral Sciences at Eastern Virginia Medical School, Norfolk, Virginia. He obtained his doctorate from Northwestern University and received postdoctoral training at the University of Toronto's Clarke Institute. Dr. Eisenberg has published extensively in the area of rehabilitation, holds editorial board positions on several journals, serves as Editor of *Rehabilitation Psychology,* and is a member of several national task forces charged with investigating various quality-of-life issues of importance to persons with chronic disabling conditions. Dr. Eisenberg is recognized at the local, regional, and national levels for his contributions to the rehabilitation of persons with physical disabilities. A Fellow and Past President of the American Psychological Association's Division of Rehabilitation Psychology, he is actively involved in heightening the public's awareness of the importance of rehabilitation through the promotion of research. In addition, he is interested in the development of standards that will establish a more effective and consistent basis for evaluating the performance of individual rehabilitation service providers.

KEY WORDS IN PSYCHOSOCIAL REHABILITATION

A Guide to Contemporary Usage

MYRON G. EISENBERG, PhD
EDITOR

WITH AN EPILOGUE BY
ROBERT L. GLUECKAUF, PhD, PURDUE UNIVERSITY

SPRINGER PUBLISHING COMPANY
NEW YORK

Springer Publishing Company, Inc.
536 Broadway
New York, NY 10012

94 95 96 97 98 / 5 4 3 2 1

Library of Congress Cataloging-in-Publication Data

Key words in psychosocial rehabilitation : a guide to
  contemporary usage / Myron G. Eisenberg, editor.
        p.   cm.
    Includes bibliographical references and index.
    ISBN 0-8261-8320-4
    1. Rehabilitation—Social aspects—Terminology.
    2. Rehabilitation—Psychological aspects—Terminology.
  I. Eisenberg, Myron G.
  RM930.K48   1994
  617'.03'014—dc20   93-23647
                                              CIP

Printed in the United States of America

To my wife, Ellen, and our daughter, Toby

CONTENTS

Abnormalization

Acceptance of Disability

Accommodation

Activities of Daily Living (ADL)

Activity Limitation

Adaptation

Adaptation Capacity

Adjustment

Ambiguity

Ambivalence-Induced Behavioral
Amplification

Americans with Disabilities Act
(ADA) of 1990

Anticipatory Grief

Appraisals

Attitude Ambivalence

Attitude Measures

Attribution

Avoidance Learning

B=F (P,O,E,)

Balance Theory of Expectations

Behavior Analysis

Behavior Modification

Biofeedback

Body Image Theory

Burnout

Caregiver Burden

Case Management

Compensatory Model

Containment

Contingency Contract

Coping

Coping vs. Succumbing
Frameworks

Crisis Theory

Devaluation

Developmental Stage Model

Disability

Disablement, Levels of

Disabling Language

Efficacy Expectations

Empowerment

Enlarging the Scope of Values

Expectation Discrepancy

Externalization

Functional Assessment

Functional Limitation

Fundamental Affective Bias

Fundamental Negative Bias

Handicap

Impairment

Independent Living

Insider versus Outsider Phenomenon

Interpersonal Theory

Just World Hypothesis

Kindness Norm

Learned Helplessness

Learned Resourcefulness

Least Restrictive Environment

Loss Resolution

Mainstreaming

Major Life Activities

Medical Model

PREFACE

Key Words In Psychosocial Rehabilitation was written as a guide
to current technical usage of words, terms, and concepts commonly found in the psychosocial rehabilitation literature. Prepared in the belief that agreement regarding conventional
meanings of words and concepts can decrease problems inherent
in communicating facts and ideas, the book's goals are to reduce
needless confusion and controversy about terms and help stabil-
ize terminology by addressing lexical and semantic difficulties.
It was secondarily prepared as a source book by serving as a
ready reference text, a starting place for investigation of unfamiliar subject matter.

There is little consensus regarding definitions—either con-
ceptional or operational—of many words commonly found in the
psychosocial rehabilitation literature, such as "adaptation,"
"adjustment," "caregiver burden," and "quality of life." Other
words, such as "handicap" and "disability," may have a meaning
for persons not familiar with psychosocial rehabilitation, concepts that are quite different from that held by those schooled in
rehabilitation theory and practice. Because the meaning of
words and terms changes depending on the context within which
they appear, *Key Words in Psychosocial Rehabilitation* offers a
nuclear definition that represents the contemporary core meaning of a cluster of potential definitions. Alternative definitions
and examples are offered in the section labeled "Usage Notes
and Comments." Finally, in the text's Epilogue, Glueckauf examines issues relevant to the client–professional communication process by considering how language influences the behavior of persons with disabilities and their families, including
that occurring in common rehabilitation situations such as
family conferences and physical therapy sessions.

In an effort to be comprehensive, a search was conducted of
the psychosocial literature. A pool of words and concepts was
developed from this review of nearly 150 publications. This list
of words and terms was then examined by members of the text's
Advisory Board who refined and revised it to include the 85
items felt to be most significant in the field. A second examination of the original list was conducted by students enrolled in

graduate-level courses, which addressed psychosocial issues in rehabilitation. They were asked to rank items in terms of their perceived importance to understanding psychosocial rehabilitation processes. These two lists, one prepared by Advisory Board members and the other developed by a cadre of students, were then combined to form the entries appearing in this book.

Intended Audience

Key Words and Concepts in Psychosocial Rehabilitation was originally designed as a reference guide for students in the behavioral and social sciences embarking on a career in rehabilitation, particularly those in such graduate programs as rehabilitation counseling, vocational rehabilitation, counseling psychology, rehabilitation psychology, and social work. The text permits them to become quickly familiar with terminology used in the clinical work site. The book, however, also was developed to be of benefit to students in physical therapy, occupational therapy, and speech therapy programs, curriculums that include coursework on the psychosocial aspects of disability. For this audience, the text provides easy access to a specialized vocabulary not otherwise available in a single, brief volume. Practitioners will also find the book to be a useful reference by providing them with an update of changing word usage. For other readers not directly involved with the psychosocial rehabilitation process, *Key Words In Psychosocial Rehabilitation* will acquaint them with a terminology found in the patient's clinical record, discussed at multidisciplinary staff meetings, considered at rounds and conferences, and appearing in scholarly publications.

STRUCTURAL PLAN

Definition. Each word, term, or concept is arranged alphabetically and defined according to its accepted and most common usage. Words having a cluster of meanings are defined by their central or core meaning. Variants of meanings are presented as secondary definitions or in the section, "Usage Notes and Comments."

Usage Notes and Comments. A discussion, explanation, or example of the word or term is provided in this section. Also considered are alternative definitions.

Cross-referencing. Where possible, related terms are identified for definition and comparison. This cross-referencing brings together terms that need to be defined in relation to each other.

References. The degree of technicality needed in a definition varies depending on who is using it. It also is true that some terms cannot be explored fully within the modest space available for its explanation here. For that reason key references are cited for most words and terms.

CONTRIBUTORS

Norman Berven, Ph.D.
Department of Studies in Behavioral Disabilities
University of Wisconsin
432 N. Murray Street
Madison, WI 53706

Brian F. Bolton, Ph.D.
Rehabilitation Research and Training Center
University of Arkansas
346 North West Avenue
Fayetteville, AR 72701

Susanne M. Bruyere, Ph.D.
Human Services Administration Program
New York State School of Industrial and Labor Relations
Extension Building, Room 105
Cornell University
Ithaca, NY 14851-0952

Susan P. Buckelew, Ph.D.
Department of Physical Medicine and Rehabilitation
Howard A. Rusk Rehabilitation Center
1 Hospital Drive
Columbia, MO 65212

Shen Hsing Annabel Chen
Department of Psychology
School of Science
Purdue University
1125 East 38th Street - KB54
Indianapolis, IN 46205-2810

Jeanne Dairaghi
Department of Psychology
School of Science
Purdue University
1125 East 38th Street - KB54
Indianapolis, IN 46205-2810

Joan E. Edelstein, M.A., P.T.
Program in Physical Therapy
Columbia University
630 West 168th Street
New York, NY 10032

M. G. Eisenberg, Ph.D.
Psychology Service
Veterans Affairs Medical Center
Hampton, VA 23667

Timothy R. Elliott, Ph.D.
University of Alabama
c/o 529 Spain Rehabilitation Center
1717 6th Avenue South
Birmingham, AL 35233-7330

Dawn M. Fekete
Department of Psychology
School of Science
Purdue University
1125 East 38th Street - KB54
Indianapolis, IN 46205-2810

Robert Glueckauf, Ph.D.
Department of Psychology
School of Science
Purdue University
1125 East 38th Street - KB54
Indianapolis, IN 46205-2810

Allen W. Heinemann, Ph.D.
Rehabilitation Services Evalua-
    tion Unit
Rehabilitation Institute of Chi-
    cago
448 East Ontario Street - Suite
    650
Chicago, IL 60611

Constance Saltz, Ph.D.
School of Social Work
University of Maryland
525 West Redwood Street
Baltimore, MD 21201-1777

Joanne E. Turnbull, Ph.D.
Western Psychiatric Institute
    and Clinic (WPIC)
3811 O'Hara Street
Pittsburgh, PA 15213-2593

Beatrice A. Wright, Ph.D.
Department of Psychology
University of Kansas
426 Fraser Hall
Lawrence, KS 66045

H. E. Yuker, Ph.D.
Center for the Study of
    Attitudes Toward Persons
    with Disabilities
Hofstra University
Hempstead, NY 11550

ACKNOWLEDGMENTS

Thanks are extended to Robert L. Glueckauf, Ph.D., whose classes in psychosocial aspects of disability at Purdue University helped identify the relative importance of words and concepts by ranking the original list of key words and terms in order of their perceived importance. This activity added a valuable student perspective to this project and helped to make the present text more meaningful and useful than it otherwise would have been. The Editor also extends sincere thanks to Norm Berven, Joan Edelstein, John Ptacek, and Dave Patterson for their thoughtful critiques of an early draft of this manuscript and their invaluable editorial comments.

KEY WORDS

ABNORMALIZATION. Ascribing supernatural powers
to explain observed behavior or accomplishments. *Usage Notes
and Comments:* An example of the abnormalization principle is
found in the belief that people who are blind must have a "sixth
sense" allowing them to perform functions believed to be impossible without sight. (*See Also:* Accommodation; Devaluation.)

Recommended Readings

Wright, B. A. (1983). *Physical disability—A psychosocial
approach* (2nd ed.). New York: Harper & Row.

ACCEPTANCE OF DISABILITY. A phenomenologi-
cal, subjective experience in which a person with a disability
develops a personally meaningful view of life following a disability. The experience is considered a process and emphasis is given
to the subjective interpretation by the person with the disability. *Usage Notes and Comments:* Initially construed as an acceptance of loss, contemporary thinking has emphasized the constructive nature of value changes often observed among persons
who have found personal meaning following acquired disability.
The process of acceptance is thought to entail the following: (1)
an enlargement of the scope of values, such that the person
perceives meaning beyond that associated with the disability;
(2) subordination of physique, as noted by the deemphasis on
physical appearance and prowess; (3) containment of disability
effects, in which the deleterious concomitants of disability are
circumscribed and do not envelope the whole of the person; and,
(4) the transformation from comparative values to asset values,
as the person emphasizes personal assets and abilities independent of perceived norms and limitations.

Research indicates that there is a positive association between
the sense of acceptance and better physical and psychosocial
adjustment (Wright, 1960). Interventions designed to foster interpersonal and social skills among persons with disabilities
often have beneficial effects on sense of acceptance, implying a
relationship between perceived competence and sense of personal meaning. The key aspect of the acceptance of disability
construct is the subjective and phenomenological process

through which a person interprets and experiences the acquired disability and subsequent value changes. (*See Also:* Accommodation: Coping; Interpersonal Theory; Quality of Life; Social Role Theory; Somatopsychology.)

References/Recommended Readings

Dembo, T., Leviton, G. L., & Wright, B. A. (1956). Adjustment to misfortune—A problem of social psychological rehabilitation. *Artificial Limbs, 3*(2), 4–62.

Glueckauf, R. L., & Quittner, A. L. (1992). Assertiveness training for disabled adults in wheelchairs: Self-report, role-play, and activity pattern outcomes. *Journal of Consulting and Clinical Psychology, 60,* 419–425.

Heinemann, A. W., McGraw, T. E., Brandt, M., & Roth, E. (1992). Prescription medication misuse among persons with spinal cord injury. *International Journal of the Addictions, 27,* 301–316.

Linkowski, D. C. (1971). A scale to measure acceptance of disability. *Rehabilitation Counseling Bulletin, 14*(4), 236–244.

Wright, B. A. (1960). *Physical disability: A psychological approach.* New York: Harper & Row.

ACCOMMODATION. The act of accommodating, the state or process of being accommodated, and a process of mutual adaptation between persons or groups that supplies a need, want, or convenience. *Usage Notes and Comments:* Within rehabilitation, the term accommodation is closely related to the principle of normalization, a concept introduced by Nirje (1969) for people who have mental handicaps. It has been extended more broadly to people with disabilities by encouraging the development of conditions of daily life that resemble the expectations of society's mainstream (Wright, 1983). This principle endorses the integration of persons with disabilities into mainstream residential, educational, employment, and social settings, separating residential and job sites for people who work in workshops, and supports the idea of calling clients in workshops, "workers."

Park (1975) defines normalization as a rational attempt to

deal with the conditions that act to support prejudice and segregate people with disabilities. Normalization may include efforts to correct wrongs of the past, bring people with disabilities into the mainstream of society, and allows for opportunities for normal risks in which failure and success are possibilities.

Stubbins (1977) highlights the sometimes unanticipated consequences of normalization and accommodation which require that some special privileges or prerogatives based on disability status be abandoned. Mainstreaming of students in public schools illustrates the trade-offs that may, on occasion, be required.

The legal concept of "reasonable accommodation" was introduced with the Rehabilitation Act of 1973, as amended, and is incorporated in the Americans with Disabilities Act (ADA, 1990). Employers, governmental agencies, and other public entities are required to make reasonable accommodation to individuals with disabilities in employment situations and with respect to public accommodation. Such accommodation refers to the adaptation of a program, facility, or work place that permits a person with a disability to participate in the program, receive the service, or perform a job. The form of these accommodations may involve changing policies, practices, or services, and using auxiliary aids such as interpreters for persons with hearing impairments; readers or taped texts for persons with visual impairments; modifying existing facilities to be readily accessible and usable by employees, and job restructuring.

Reasonable accommodations are to be provided to "qualified" persons with disabilities; that is, persons who are otherwise qualified to perform a job or benefit from a service because they meet all other qualifications of the job or services. The reasonableness of accommodations in employment settings is determined on an individual basis that reflects job requirements, an employee's or applicant's disability, and the degree to which modifications or aids would pose an undue hardship on an employer. In issues related to public accommodations, the extent of difficulty or expense is considered in defining undue burden. (*See Also:* Americans with Disability Act of 1990; Normalization; Reasonable Accommodation; Qualified Handicapped Person.)

6   accommodation

References/Recommended Readings

Americans with Disabilities Act of 1990, 42 U.S.C., S12101 Note.

Americans with Disabilities Act: ADA Compliance Guide. (1990). Washington, DC: Thompson Publishing Group.

Nirje, B. (1969). The normalization principle and its human management implications. In R. B. Kugel & W. Wolfensberger (Eds.), *Changing patterns in residential services for the mentally retarded* (pp. 179–195). Washington, DC: U.S. Government Printing Office.

Park, L. D. (1975). Barriers to normality for the handicapped. *Rehabilitation Literature, 36,* 108–111.

Stubbins, J. (1977). *Social and psychological aspects of disability: A handbook for practitioners.* Baltimore: University Park Press.

Wright, B. A. (1983). *Physical disability: A psychosocial approach* (2nd ed.). New York: Harper & Row.

ACTIVITIES OF DAILY LIVING (ADL). Range of common activities in which performance is required for self-maintenance and independent community residence. *Usage Notes and Comments:* Activities of daily living are typically divided into three categories: (1) physical ADL (sometimes simply called ADL), which refers to the most basic of personal care tasks; (2) instrumental ADL, which is concerned with more complex activities needed for independent living; and, (3) mobility (ability to negotiate one's environment), which may also be a component of the first two categories.

Several instruments have been developed to assess competence in ADL. Of particular note in the area of physical ADL (PADL) is the scale developed by Katz and his colleagues (Katz & Akpom, 1976) and the adaptations of the Barthel and PULSES[1] scales (each of which also includes assessment of mobility) by Granger and his colleagues (Granger & Greer, 1976). The Katz scale focuses on ability to perform six activities without aid. These activities can be ordered hierarchically and include feeding, continence, transferring (moving in and out of

[1]Physical condition, Upper extremities, Lower extremities, Sensory, Excretory, mental and emotional Status.

bed or chair), attending to self at the toilet, dressir
ing. The Barthel scale covers the same general
greater detail. Feeding, for instance, is subdivided in
from a cup and feeding from a dish, and four specific types ʋ.
transfers are described. PULSES, on the other hand, focuses less
on specific tasks and more on the personal physical characteristics that make task completion difficult, thereby indicating
which areas of the body might be targeted for rehabilitation
interventions. PULSES also examines social functioning.

Developments in assessment of instrumental ADL (IADL)
have been provided by Lawton & Brody (1969). These investigators constructed two gender-specific Guttman scaled
measures that assess the handling of personal finances, preparing meals, shopping, traveling, and doing housework.

ADL assessments differ with regard to the level of specificity
of performance of the targeted activity and the categories used
to assess adequacy of performance. The categories may range
from the general (e.g., can do unaided versus other) to more
detailed (Kane & Kane, 1984). Three-point categories, however,
would seem to be the easiest to use (i.e., can do unaided, needs
help, can't do) and provide enough information to be useful. The
categories may distinguish among the types of help used (e.g.,
can do with device, needs help from a person), with mechanical
devices recognized as providing greater independence than help
from another person. Assessment may be conducted by the person who is involved, a family member, or a service provider with
each of the three providing different perspectives and different
information. Assessment is ideally based on observation of actual performance, but often is not, as in cases when the person
being assessed is not permitted to perform the activity or does
not have access to the necessary facilities or resources (e.g.,
where unattended bathing is not allowed, where there are no
cooking facilities). In this case, assessment may reflect hopeful
expectation. Some scales are more concerned with testing a
range of motor abilities than with the variety of activities necessary for functioning in society. This may have particular relevance for rehabilitation, but alone can rarely indicate service
need or appropriate residential setting. ADL assessments are
rarely designed such that environmental factors that might
affect performance are considered.

ADLs are central to any assessment of level of personal independent functioning. Information on ADL capacity has been used more extensively, and for a greater variety of purposes, than has information from any other type of assessment. Such assessments have been used for a variety of purposes which include: (1) to indicate individual social, mental, and physical functioning; (2) for diagnosis; (3) to determine service requirement and impact; (4) to guide service initiation and completion; (5) to estimate the level of qualifications needed in a provider; (6) to assess need for environmental supports; (7) to justify residential location; (8) to provide a basis for personnel employment decisions; (9) to determine service changes and provide arguments for reimbursement; and, (10) to estimate categorical eligibility for specific services (e.g., attendant allowances). (*See Also:* Adaptation; Functional Assessment; Functional Limitation.)

References

Granger, C. V., & Greer, D. S. (1976). Functional status measurement and medical rehabilitation outcomes. *Archives of Physical Medicine and Rehabilitation, 57,* 103–109.

Kane, R. A., & Kane, R. L. (1984). *Assessing the elderly: A practical guide to measurement.* Lexington, MA: Lexington Books.

Katz, S., & Akpom, C. A. (1976). A measure of primary sociobiological functions. *International Journal of Health Services, 6,* 493–507.

Lawton, M. P., & Brody, E. M. (1969). Assessment of older people: Self-maintaining and instrumental activities of daily living. *Gerontologist, 9,* 179–186.

ACTIVITY LIMITATION.   A measure of disability defined as long-term reduction in activity resulting from chronic disease or impairment. *Usage Notes and Comments:* In its annual National Health Interview Survey (NHIS), the National Center for Health Statistics (NCHS) describes a limitation in terms of the *major activity* it considers usual for one's age group: (1) play typical for children under 5 years of age, (2) attending school for those 5–17 years of age, (3) working or keeping house for persons 18–69 years of age, and (4) capacity for independent living (e.g., the ability to bathe, shop, dress, eat, and otherwise care for oneself without the assistance of another person) for persons after age 69.

If persons are not limited in their major activity, the NCHS asks if they are limited in other ways, which it also calls *nonmajor* or *outside* activity. Such activities might include social, civic, or recreational endeavors and are normally less important than major ones. However, for those 18–69 years of age who keep house, and persons 70 years of age and over, measures of outside activity also include the ability to work.

Using this definitional schema, the NCHS estimates that 14.1% of the U.S. population have an *activity limitation* (National Institute on Disability and Rehabilitation Research, 1992). This includes 4.1% who are unable to independently carry on their major activity, 5.4% who are limited in the amount or kind of major activity, and 4.5% who are not limited in their major activity but are limited in their secondary activity. (*See Also:* Americans with Disabilities Act of 1990; Disability; Functional Limitation; Work Disability.)

References

National Institute on Disability and Rehabilitation Research. (1992). *Digest of data on persons with disabilities*. Washington, DC: U.S. Department of Education.

ADAPTATION. (1) A condition that meets two criteria: (a) the individual meets the demands of the environment; and, (b) the individual experiences a sense of general well-being in relation to the environment (George, 1980). (2) An intrapsychic evaluation of general life quality that is operationalized through such concepts as morale, life satisfaction, and happiness. *Usage Notes and Comments:* Adaption's opposite, maladaption, occurs if the individual cannot meet the level of environmental demand or can do so only at the cost of personal well-being. Adaptation thus has both objective and subjective components. The degree to which the individual meets environmental demands is an objective phenomenon, whereas perceptions of well-being are subjective. George (1980) points out that the aspect of this definition that distinguishes adaptation from other concepts (such as life satisfaction and functional status), is the explicit statement that capacity must be assessed in relation to environmental demands.

There is little consensus regarding definition—either conceptual or operational—of adaptation as it is used in psychosocial rehabilitation research. Several investigators have attempted to define the concept in objective terms, focusing on parameters such as health and functional status. In general though, adaptation has been used as an overall rubric for understanding the well-being of persons with disabilities rather than as a theoretically and operationally distinct concept. This results in difficulty when trying to compare and integrate results across studies that have operationalized adaptation in diverse ways. (*See Also:* Accommodation; Activities of Daily Living; Activity Capacity; Adjustment; Coping; Learned Resourcefulness; Quality of Life.)

References

George, L. K. (1980). *Role transitions in later life: A social stress perspective*. Monterey, CA: Brooks/Cole.

ADAPTIVE CAPACITY. The ability to monitor performance in the face of altered circumstances. (*See Also:* Adaptation; Accommodation; Adjustment; Coping; Coping Framework.)

Recommended Reading

Shock, N. W. (1987). Adaptive capacity. In G. L. Maddox (Ed.), *Encyclopedia of aging*. New York: Springer Publishing Co.

ADJUSTMENT (to disability). (1) To bring into balance or achieve homeostasis after a disruption. (2) The process of establishing an identity that provides meaning and quality to life. *Usage Notes and Comments:* The term "adjustment" is used frequently in the rehabilitation literature; however, there is no one accepted definition. Trieschmann (1988) uses the term "adjusted" synonymously with "rehabilitated" and cautions that both concepts represent a process rather than an endpoint.

Prior to 1950, adjustment was often viewed as a mental trait. In recent decades, there has been greater emphasis on viewing adjustment as an interaction between the person and environment. For instance, Wright (1983) proposes that behavioral responses are integrated in response to environmental pressures and internal mental processes. Although Wright identifies positive personal adjustment with self-esteem, her theory stresses the influence of physical and interpersonal environment.

Adjustment can also be viewed as a comprehensive health status variable that is not restricted to internal processes. Trieschmann (1988), for example, outlines three major aspects of behavioral components to adjustment, including: (1) survival activities; (2) harmonious living and working environment; and, (3) productivity. (*See Also:* Accommodation; Adaptive Capacity; B=F[P,O,E]; Coping; Developmental Stage Models.)

References/Recommended Readings

Shontz, F. C. (1984). Psychological adjustment to physical disability: Trends in theories. In R. P. Marinelli, & A. E. Dell Orto (Eds.), *The psychological and social impact of physical disability* (2nd ed.) (pp. 119–126). New York: Springer Publishing Co.

Trieschmann, R. B. (1988). *Spinal cord injuries: Psychological, social, and vocational rehabilitation* (2nd ed.) New York: Demos Publications.

Wright, B. A. (1983) *Physical disability—A psychosocial approach.* (2nd ed.) New York: Harper & Row.

AMBIGUITY. Uncertainty or lack of clarity in situations, roles, and behavior. *Usage Notes and Comments:* Ambiguity can occur among rehabilitation professionals when there is unclear communication and role assignment (Ursprung, 1986). Kahn, Wold, Quinn, Snock, and Rosenthal (1964) have shown that role ambiguity leads to increased tension and anxiety, as well as decrements in role performance. For individuals with disabilities, ambiguity may occur at diagnosis or onset of disability. When characteristics of the medical condition are not clearly explained, persons with disabilities may be unsure of what to expect and, consequently, may become fearful or anxious (Martin, 1988). Ambiguity may also arise when an individual's expectations about the conduct of treatment do not coincide with the behavior of health care professionals. For example, in counseling persons with disabilities who are of Chinese American descent, the client-centered approach used by many rehabilitation counselors may be viewed as ambiguous and unsatisfactory. This is due to traditional Chinese society's emphasis on well-defined and structured social relationships (Chan, Lam, Wong, Leung, & Fang, 1988). Rehabilitation research has primarily focused on identifying factors that contribute to perceptions of ambiguity and on developing strategies to decrease those ambiguities. (*See Also:* Ambivalence-Induced Behavioral Amplification; Attitude Ambivalence.)

References

Chan, F., Lam, C. S., Wong, D., Leung, P., & Fang, X. S. (1988). Counseling Chinese Americans with disabilities. *Journal of Applied Rehabilitation Counseling, 19,* 21–25.

Kahn, R. L., Wold, D. M., Quinn, R. P., Snock, J. D., & Rosenthal, R. A. (1964). *Organizational stress.* New York: Wiley.

Martin, D. A. (1988). Children and adolescents with traumatic brain injury: Impact on the family. *Journal of Learning Disabilities, 21,* 464–470.

Ursprung, A. W. (1986). Incidence and correlates of burnout in residential service settings. *Rehabilitation Counseling Bulletin, 29,* 225–239.

AMBIVALENCE-INDUCED BEHAVIORAL AMPLIFICATION.

A theory which maintains that attitudes toward certain groups in society such as individuals with physical disabilities, older adults, racial and ethnic minority groups, and persons with mental disabilities, tend to be ambivalent rather than simply positive or negative. *Usage Notes and Comments:* This theory, introduced by Katz (1981), maintains that conflicted attitudes about persons with disabilities may generate tension in the individual that can be resolved by amplifying one component of the attitude while suppressing the other contradictory component. Behaviorally, the resolution of this tension may entail an amplified response toward persons with disabilities, either positive or negative, depending on the situation.

Evidence of behavioral extremity has been found when the individual has a physical disability. For example, Katz, Glass, Lucido, and Farber (1979) found that study participants gave more help to a confederate using a wheelchair than to a confederate who did not use a wheelchair, after they had unintentionally harmed her. A similar amplification effect was obtained when, instead of compensatory helping, the available response option was an opportunity to denigrate the person (Katz, Glass, Lucido, & Farber, 1977). (*See Also:* Ambiguity; Attitude Ambivalence.)

References/Recommended Readings

Baly, J. W. (1991). Evaluation of a task partner who does or does not have a physical disability: Response amplification or sympathy effect. *Rehabilitation Psychology, 36*(2), 99–110.

Katz, I. (1981). *Stigma: A social psychological analysis.* Hillsdale, NJ: Lawrence Elbaum Associates.

Katz, I., Glass, D. C., Lucido, D. J., & Farber, J. (1977). Ambivalence, guilt and denigration of a physically handicapped victim. *Journal of Personality, 43*, 419–429.

Katz, I., Glass, D. C., Lucido, D. J., & Farber, J. (1979). Harmdoing and the victim's racial or orthopedic stigma as determinants of helping behavior. *Journal of Personality, 47*, 340–364.

AMERICANS WITH DISABILITIES ACT (ADA) OF 1990.

An Act signed into law on July 27, 1990, which guarantees the rights of persons with disabilities to be free of discrimination by private employers, private health service providers, or private facilities with public access. *Usage Notes and Comments:* The Americans with Disabilities Act serves two purposes. First, it clarifies federal protection for individuals with disabilities that exists under the Rehabilitation Act of 1973. Second, it extends protection to those never before covered under federal law. Federal protection against discrimination has its roots in various Civil Rights Acts that made it illegal to discriminate on the basis of race, creed, sex, and national origin. However, it was not until 1973, with passage of the Vocational Rehabilitation and Other Rehabilitation Services statute (popularly known as the Vocational Rehabilitation Act or the Rehabilitation Act of 1973), that federal law prohibited employers who received funds from federal programs to discriminate against individuals with disabilities. Although this Act went a long way toward acknowledging that Americans with disabilities had been unfairly victimized, it fell short of extending the complete protection of the law that already existed for those who experienced other types of discrimination. Indeed, although members of religious sects and people of various ethnicity (of either gender) were enjoying the same access to privately funded public services as white male citizens, those with disabilities could not, and did not, consider themselves protected by federal law. For persons with chronic conditions, The Americans with Disabilities Act (ADA) provides the most comprehensive protection from discrimination to date.

Section 1 of the ADA sets forth the short title and the table of contents. Section 2 states the findings and purposes of the Act, and Section 3 defines terms in accordance with the Act. Under Section 3, a disability is defined as: "(a) a physical or mental impairment that substantially limits one or more of the major life activities of such individual; (b) a record of such an impairment; or (c) being regarded as having such an impairment." The first prong of the definition is meant to include both physical and mental impairments.

A physical or mental impairment means (1) any physiological disorder or condition, cosmetic disfigurement, or anatomical loss affecting one or more of the following body systems: neurological; musculoskeletal; special sense organs; respiratory, including speech organs; cardiovascular; reproductive, digestive; genitourinary; hemic and lymphatic; skin; and endocrine; or (2) any mental or psychological disorder, such as mental retardation, organic brain syndrome, emotional or mental illness, and specific learning disabilities.

For the purposes of the ADA, a physical or mental impairment is not considered a disability under the first prong of the definition unless it "substantially limits a major life activity." A "major life activity" includes such functions as seeing, hearing, walking, speaking, breathing, learning, performing manual tasks, and caring for oneself. For example, a person with paraplegia is substantially limited in the major life activity of walking, a person who is blind is substantially limited in the major life activity of seeing, and a person who is mentally retarded is substantially challenged in the major life activity of learning. Minor, trivial impairments do not substantially limit major life activities. The proper test is whether the "individual's important life activities are restricted as to the conditions, manner, or duration under which they can be performed in comparison to most people."

The second prong of the definition includes someone with "a record of such an impairment" as a person with a disability. Thus, the definition extends protection to persons who have recovered from impairments or who have been misclassified as having an impairment. The third test, "being regarded as having such an impairment," applies regardless of whether a person has an impairment. Focus is placed on whether an individual is treated as if he or she had an impairment that substantially limits a major life activity. (*See Also:* Activity Limitations; Disability; Disablement, Levels of; Handicap; Impairment; Major Life Activity; Least Restrictive Environment; Reasonable Accommodation; Qualified Handicapped Person; Vocational Rehabilitation Act of 1973.)

Recommended Readings

Bruyere, S. (Guest Ed.). (1993). Implications of the Americans with Disabilities Act of 1990 for psychologists (special issue). *Rehabilitation Psychology, 38*(2).

Gerson, H. E., & Addison, J. G. (1991). Handicapped discrimination law and the Americans with Disabilities Act. *Mississippi College Law Review,* Spring, 233–253.

Law, S. K. (1991). The Americans with Disabilities Act of

1990; Burden on business or dignity for the disabled? *Duquesne Law Review,* Fall, 99–114.

Mahoney, R. E., & Gibofsky, A. (1992). The Americans with Disabilities Act of 1990. *Journal of Legal Medicine, 13,* 51–75.

Thunder, J. M. (1992). The Americans with Disabilities Act: From policy to practice. *Federal Bar News and Journal, 1,* 106–107.

ANTICIPATORY GRIEF. The process of being confronted with impending loss and initiating the grieving process before the event actually occurs. *Usage Notes and Comments:* Theoretically, anticipatory grief is assumed to be beneficial because an individual experiences emotions prior to the actual occurrence of the loss, providing an opportunity to rehearse roles associated with bereavement and begin to master the profound changes that accompany the loss, thus mitigating the trauma associated with loss and diminishing grief.

The term can be applied to death as well as to the partial losses associated with chronic illnesses and disabilities (Gallagher, 1985). Glick, Weiss, and Parkes (1974) postulate that grief is shorter and predicts a greater cognitive and emotional reorganization following the loss when there has been anticipation. Others (cf. Rosen, 1990) believe that anticipatory grief does not guarantee a lessening of pain or shortened duration of the grieving period, but hold that anticipatory grief has benefits for both the practical and emotional sphere of life. For example, personal planning can occur, such as resolving interpersonal conflicts and attending to practical considerations (e.g., financial arrangements). (*See Also:* Loss Resolution.)

References

Glick, I. O., Weiss, R. S., & Parkes, C. M. (1974). *The first year of bereavement.* New York: Wiley.

Gallagher, D. E. (1985). Intervention strategies to assist caregivers of frail elders: Current research status and future research directions. In C. Eisdorfer, M. P. Lawton, & G. Maddox (Eds.), *Annual Review of Gerontology and Geriatrics,* (Vol. 5, pp. 249–282). New York: Springer Publishing Co.

R. S. Lazarus (1991). *Emotion and adaptation.* New York: Oxford University Press.

Lindemann, E. (1944). The symptomatology and management of acute grief. *American Journal of Psychiatry, 101,* 141–148.

Rosen, E. J. (1990). *Families facing death.* New York: Lexington.

APPRAISALS. The cognitive process through which individuals evaluate their physical, social, and psychological environments as well as events around them. *Usage Notes and Comments:* Cognitive appraisal is hypothesized to play an important mediating role in the stress, coping, and outcome process. According to Lazarus and his colleagues (Lazarus, 1990, 1991; Lazarus & Folkman, 1984), people base their coping efforts largely on their interpretations of the event and the personal and social resources available to deal with the event as construed. People's efforts to cope, in turn, relate to the outcome of the stressful transaction.

Although cognitive appraisals occur more or less continuously, several distinct phases have been identified. When people first enter into a transaction with the envirnoment, they evaluate what is at stake in the situation. These primary appraisals often take the form of "What do I have to gain or lose in this situation?" These appraisals usually occur in conjuction with secondary appraisals, which involve an evaluation of the social and personal resources available to deal with the event and an examination of the available coping options. In essence, the person asks him/herself, "What if anything can be done about it?" (Lazarus & Folkman, 1984).

Cognitive appraisal is an important component of the rehabilitation process because research indicates that certain types of appraisals are associated with more or less adaptive coping responses (Lazarus & Folkman, 1984). For instance, a person who was recently disabled and who views the event in terms of loss will likely cope differently than if he/she had viewed the event as a challenge to be overcome. A loss appraisal will likely be met with emotion-focused coping efforts such as avoidance, blaming self, or wishful thinking. A challenge appraisal, however, will likely be met with active, problem-focused coping methods including goal setting, planning, and active participation in the rehabilitation process.

References

Lazarus, R. S. (1990). Stress, coping and illness. In H. S. Friedman (Ed.), *Personality and disease* (pp. 97–120). New York: Wiley.

Lazarus, R. S. (1991). *Emotion and adaptation.* New York: Oxford University Press.

Lazarus, R. S., & Folkman, S. (1984). *Stress, appraisal, and coping.* New York: Springer Publishing Co.

ATTITUDE AMBIVALENCE. A concept which states that members of groups perceived as having marginal status in a society (e.g., persons with disabilities, members of racial or ethnic minority groups, persons with drug or alcohol addictions) tend to be stigmatized and perceived by others as both deviant and disadvantaged. As a consequence of these perceptions, attitudes toward group members tend to involve contradictions and attitudinal ambivalence. *Usage Notes and Comments:* The concept of attitude ambivalence is demonstrated in the attitudes of some members of families that include children with disabilities. Positive attitudes of love, compassion, and caring may co-exist with negative attitudes of rejection or resentment. As a consequence, overt verbalized expressions of attitudes toward persons with disabilities are often positive, whereas negative feelings of rejection tend not to be expressed. Awareness of these ambivalent attitudes may lead to a state of tension. (*See Also:* Ambiguity; Ambivalence-Induced Behavioral Amplification.)

References

Barker, R. G., Wright, B. A., Meyerson, L., & Gonick, M. R. (1953). *Adjustment to physical handicap and illness.* New York: Social Science Research Council.

Goffman, E. (1963). *Stigma: Notes on the management of spoiled identity.* Englewood Cliffs, NJ: Prentice-Hall.

Katz, I., Hass, R. G., & Bailey, J. (1988). Attitudinal ambivalence and behavior toward people with disabilities. In H. E. Yuker (Ed.), *Attitudes toward persons with disabilities: Progress and Prospects* (pp. 47–58). New York: Springer Publishing Co.

ATTITUDE MEASURES. Instruments used to assess attitudes. *Usage Notes and Comments:* Although attitude scales are the best known attitudinal measurement techniques, other techniques are used to measure attitudes and include interviews, adjective check lists, the semantic differential, social distance scales, and sociometric measures (Antonak, 1988).

An *attitude scale* involves the use of definite rules in the construction and evaluation of responses to a set of questions relating to a specific topic. Although there are many scales for measuring attitudes toward persons with disabilities, only a few have been extensively used in research. One of the best known and most used is the Attitudes Toward Disabled Persons scale (ATDP, Yuker & Block, 1986). Also widely used are the Disability Factor Scales (DFS, Siller, Chipman, Ferguson, & Vann, 1967). Another measure of attitudes toward persons with mental illness includes the Opinions about Mental Illness scale (OMI, Cohen & Struening, 1962). Each of these scales is reliable and valid and has been used in many studies over the past 30 years. New instruments, including multivariate scales, have been developed in recent years.

Interviews may be either carefully structured with specific carefully worded questions or free form in which the interviewer can ask any questions that seem to be pertinent. Unfortunately, interviews often yield data of unknown reliability and validity and consequently are of limited use.

Adjective check lists ask the respondent to check those adjectives from an alphabetical list of 20 to 300 that describe a person with a specific disability. Use of such lists provide a description of the stereotypical views of persons with disabilities. (Antonak, 1988).

Semantic differential scales were described and popularized by Osgood, Suci, and Tannenbaum (1957). In using this method, a single concept such as "Person with a Disability" or "Person who is Hearing Impaired" is presented at the top of a page, followed by pairs of bipolar adjectives connected by a line with marked intervals. Respondents are asked to check the box or mark the line at the point that represents their rating of the concept on each scale.

Social distance scales, first used by Bogardus (1925), were initially used to measure attitudes toward ethnic groups. Respondents are asked to use a 7-point scale to indicate the closest relationship they are willing to have with members of a specific group, (e.g. persons who are developmentally delayed).

Sociometric measures are used mainly with children to determine how a person behaves or intends to behave toward a particular attitude referent when given a choice of behaviors. MacMillan and Morrison (1984) discuss sociometric research with a variety of groups and areas within special education and rehabilitation.

Multidimensional scaling is a relatively new technique that seeks to include measures of the several different dimensions involved in the perception of disabilities such as physical versus other types of disability, cognitive factors, behavioral-emotional factors, and normality versus deviance factors (Schmelkin, 1988).

References/Recommended Readings

Antonak, R. F. (1988). Methods to measure attitudes toward people who are disabled. In H. E. Yuker (Ed.), *Attitudes toward persons with disabilities*. New York: Springer Publishing Co.

Atchley, R. C. (1985). *Social forces and aging*, 4th ed. Belmont, CA: Wadsworth.

Bogardus, E. S. (1925). Measuring social distances. *Journal of Applied Sociology, 9,* 216–226.

Cohen, J. S., & Struening, E. L. (1962). Opinions about mental illness in the personnel of two large mental hospitals. *Journal of Abnormal and Social Psychology, 64,* 349–360.

Glenn, N. D. (1980). Values, attitudes, and beliefs. In O. G. Brim, Jr., & J. Kagan (Eds.), *Constancy and change in human development* (pp. 596–640). Cambridge, MA: Harvard University Press.

Kogan, J. (1979). Beliefs, attitudes, and stereotypes about old people: A new look at some old issues. *Research on Aging, 1*(1), 11–36.

MacMillan, D. L., & Morrison, G. M. (1984). *Sociometric research in special education: Theory and practice* (pp. 70–92). Reston, VA: Council for Exceptional Children.

Osgood, C. E., Suci, G. L., & Tannenbaum, P. H. (1957). *The measurement of meaning.* Urbana, IL: University of Illinois.

Schmelkin, L. P. (1988). Multidimensional perspectives in the perception of disabilities. In H. E. Yuker (Ed.), *Attitudes toward persons with disabilities: Progress and prospects.* New York: Springer Publishing Co.

Siller, J., Chipman, A., Ferguson, L. T., & Vann, D. H. (1967). Attitudes of the nondisabled toward the physically disabled. *Studies in reactions to disability: XI.* New York: New York University School of Education.

Yuker, H. E., & Block, J. R. (1986). *Research with the Attitude Toward Disabled Persons Scales: 1960–1985.* Hempstead, NY: Hofstra University Center for the Study of Attitudes toward Persons with Disabilities.

ATTRIBUTION. A social psychological process through which individuals come to believe that certain events, actions, or characteristics are linked to the behavior of self or others. *Usage Notes and Comments:* Attributions help explain our behavior and the behavior of others and are frequently used to predict future behavior. Wright (1983) notes that attributional processes are of special interest to rehabilitation because they may lead to inaccurate assessment of self or others. For example, in a study on "self-blame" attributions for disability and perceived rehabilitation outcomes, Bordieri and colleagues (Bordieri, Comninel, & Drehmer, 1989; Bordieri & Kilbury, 1991) found that clients who were perceived as making the least accurate attributions were rated as having less effective coping methods, a less favorable rehabilitation prognosis, and less control over future life events than clients who made more accurate attributions.

Negative outcomes may also occur as a result of repetitive attributions of responsibility to external circumstances or events. Learned helplessness, the belief that one has no control over a situation, is a potential result if individuals repeatedly attribute their disability to something beyond their control or ability to solve (Justice, 1988). (*See Also:* Learned Helplessness; Self-Efficacy theory; Coping.)

References/Recommended Readings

Bordieri, J. E., Comninel, M. E., & Drehmer, D. E. (1989). Client attributions for disability: Perceived accuracy, adjustment, and coping. *Rehabilitation Psychology, 34*(4), 271–277.

Bordieri, J. E., & Kilbury, R. (1991). Self-blame attributions for disability and perceived rehabilitation outcomes. *Rehabilitation Counseling Bulletin, 34*(4), 320–331.

Brewin, C., & Antaki, C. (1987). An analysis of ordinary explanations in clinical attribution research. *Journal of Social and Clinical Psychology, 5,* 79–98.

Gatchel, R. J., Baum, A., & Krantz, D. S. (1989). *An introduction to health psychology* (2nd ed.). New York: Random House.

Janoff-Bulman, R. (1979). Characterological versus behavioral self-blame: Inquiries into depression and rape. *Journal of Personality and Social Psychology, 33,* 195–206.

Justice, B. (1988). *Who gets sick: How beliefs, moods, and thoughts affect our health.* Los Angeles: Jeremy P. Tarcher.

Wright, B. A. (1983). *Physical disability—A psychosocial approach* (2nd ed.). Philadelphia: Harper & Row.

AVOIDANCE LEARNING. A phenomenon that typically occurs in response to actual or perceived aversive events (Stoyva, 1981), whereby the individual develops a specific set of responses to reduce the likelihood of coming into contact with the aversive stimulus or event (Gordon, 1989). *Usage Notes and Comments:* An example of avoidance learning follows. A person whose mobility is confined to a wheelchair may anticipate social rejection and, as an anticipatory response, avoid interactions with other people. Avoidance learning can also lead to both negative and positive consequences. For example, an individual with schizophrenia may routinely experience increased feelings of paranoia prior to relapse. Through avoidance learning, he/she may reduce the possibility of relapse by avoiding situations that increase paranoia, such as going to a crowded mall. On the other hand, an individual who is receiving chemotherapy and experiencing aversive side effects may learn to avoid the treatment to reduce the side effects.

References

Gordon, W. C. (1989). *Learning and memory.* Pacific Grove, CA: Brooks/Cole.

Stoyva, J. (1981). Learning principles, biofeedback, and behavioral medicine. In R. C. Simons, (Ed.), *Understanding
human behavior in health and illness* (pp. 552–562). Baltimore, MD: Williams & Wilkins.

B=F(P,O,E). A formula used to describe the balance
among variables that determine health status wherein behavior
(B) or health is seen as a function of the interaction of psychosocial (P), biological-organic (O), and environmental (E) influences. *Usage Notes and Comments:* The formula B=F(P,O,E)
represents an attempt to graphically display a mind–body system. Variables in the system are shown below (Trieschmann,
1987b, p. 47):

Psychosocial variables (P)	Organic variables (O)	Environmental variables (E)
Responsibility for self	Intelligence and cognitive ability	Income
Will to live	Endurance	Transportation
Social skills	Strength	Architectural and geographic barriers
Style of coping with stress	Perceptual motor coordination	Access to knowledgeable health professionals
Locus of control (I-E)	Aptitudes	Educational and vocational resources
Self-confidence	Extent of physical impairment	Financial disincentives
Judgment	Sensory abilities	Family and interpersonal support
Problem-solving ability	Bladder and bowel control	Socioeconomic status
Education	Respiratory function	Availability of physical assistance (if needed)
Work history	Pain	Behavioral supervision (if needed)
Job skills	General health status	Payment for medical care
Cultural and ethnic group		Role models
Gender		
Creativity		

Psychosocial variables (P) include all of the intrinsic characteristics that might be subsumed under the construct of per-

sonality. Organic (O) or biological variables include those body and mental functions that derive from genetic, environmental, and behavioral lifestyle influences. Rather than being static, these organic variables change according to age, health, and general well-being. Environmental (E) variables are those factors distal to the person that determine whether or not a physical impairment will become a handicap in achieving health, well-being, and productivity. The variables may serve as assets or liabilities to function and, thus, are critical parameters in the feedback loop among P, O, and E variables. Because the human being is a complex whole, none of the above variables is considered to be separate and uninfluenced by the entire equation. An example drawn from Wright (1983) helps illustrate this equation. A person with impaired hearing may find it difficult to communicate in a noisy room but not in a quiet room, an observation that immediately highlights environmental aspects of the problem. A general question one could ask to help reveal possible situational contributions to a problem is as follows: Does the person behave this way or have a problem in all situations? A "no" answer means that the behavior depends at least partially on the situation. Technically speaking, covariation between behavior and situation begins to emerge (pp. 33-34). (*See also:* Medical Model.)

References/Recommended Readings

Lewin, K. (1936). *Principles of topological psychology.* New York: McGraw-Hill.

Trieschmann, R. B. (1987a). *Spinal cord injuries: The psychological, social, and vocational adjustment.* New York: Demos Publications.

Trieschmann, R. B. (1987b). *Aging with a disability.* New York: Demos Publications.

Wright, B. A. (1983). *Physical disability—A psychosocial approach.* New York: Harper & Row.

BALANCE THEORY OF EXPECTATIONS. A
theory developed by Heider (1958) which contends that pain and suffering are subjectively equated with punishment or trial by

ordeal, while the expectation of relief is subjectively equivalent to purification and exoneration. *Usage Notes and Comments:* Negative explanations for suffering are balanced by positive expectations for relief. When relief occurs and individuals find themselves unchanged, the expected balance is disconfigured and disruption of behavior follows.

References/Recommended Readings

English, R. W. (1977). The application of personality theory to explain psychological reactions to physical disability. In R. P. Marinelli & A. E. Dell Orto (Eds.), *The psychological and social aspects of physical disability* (pp. 90–129). New York: Springer Publishing Co.
Heider, F. (1958). *The psychology of interpersonal relations.* New York: Wiley.

BEHAVIOR MODIFICATION. (1) A treatment modality that emphasizes the social–environmental causation of human behavior. (2) Viewing ineffective or maladaptive behavior as learned, and thus amenable to change by altering the environmental contingencies controlling the behavior. *Usage Notes and Comments:* The theoretical foundation of behavior modification derives from several sources: principles of conditioning (e.g., Pavlov, 1960), learning theory (e.g., Bandura, 1969; Hull, 1943; Wolpe, 1982), and the application of experimental lab procedures to human problems (e.g., Skinner, 1938). Behavior modification techniques (e.g., shaping, systematic desensitization, modeling) usually focus on specific, observable symptoms or behaviors as targets for change. The behavior therapist designs interventions based on psychological learning theory and/or experimental lab evidence and monitors progress continuously and quantitatively. Behavior modification focuses on reinforcement or punishment. Reinforcement can be positive (the presentation of which results in the increase in the frequency of responding), or negative (the withdrawal of which results in an increase in the frequency of a response). Punishment involves either the withdrawal of a positive reinforcer or the presentation of a punisher, which typically results in a decrease in the targeted behavior. Also important are schedules of reinforcement (fixed, variable, ratio, or interval) and extinction (a process whereby responses decline in frequency as a consequence of no longer being reinforced).

Behavior modification is used in a variety of ways in working with people with disabilities—in psychological counseling as well as in physical therapy, occupational therapy, and speech therapy. Some of the ways these techniques can be used include teaching people with developmental disabilities to learn a new job, helping people with traumatic brain injury to readjust to the home environment, teaching people to overcome phobias, and increasing compliance. (*See Also:* Behavioral Analysis; Contingency Contract.)

References/Recommended Readings

Bandura, A. (1969). *Principles of behavior modification.* New York: Holt, Rinehart and Winston.

Hull, C. (1943). *Principles of behavior: An introduction to behavior therapy.* New York: Appleton-Century Crofts.

Ince, L. (1976). *Behavior modification in rehabilitation.* Springfield, IL: Charles C Thomas.

Kanfer, F., & Phillips, J. (1970). *Learning foundations of behavior therapy.* New York: Wiley.

Pavlov, I. (1960). *Conditioned reflexes: An investigation of the physiological activity of the cerebral cortex.* New York: Dover Publications.

Skinner, B. (1938). *The behavior of organisms: An experimental analysis.* New York: Appleton-Century Crofts.

Wolpe, J. (1982). *The practice of behavior therapy* (3rd ed.). New York: Pergamon Press.

BEHAVIORAL ANALYSIS. Identification of problematic behaviors and factors responsible for behavior change through objective observations and quantitative recordings. *Usage Notes and Comments:* Typically, behavioral analysis is expressed in an A-B-C format, in which the antecedents (A) and consequences (C) of the behavior (B) are noted, as well as the behavior itself. Presenting problematic behaviors are analyzed with regard to their nature and frequency of occurrence and the conditions operating to reinforce them. Further, factors operating to punish adaptive behaviors are isolated and effective behaviors in the person's repertoire are selected as competing responses, or as reinforcing stimuli for more adaptive behavioral patterns (Nicoholi, 1978).

In rehabilitation, behavioral analysis is often applied as a systematic procedure used to assess the functioning and abilities of individuals with disabilities through observation of behavior. For example, an analysis for a person with chronic back pain might involve what environmental factors reinforce pain behaviors (e.g., spouse solicitude) as well as activity schedules designed to exacerbate fatigue. Behavioral analysis is often coupled with goal setting to enhance social and recreational skills (Halpern & Fuhrer, 1984). (*See Also:* Behavior Modification; Contingency Contract; Functional Assessment.)

References/Recommended Readings

Emerson, E., & McGill, P. (1989). Normalization and applied behavior analysis: Values and technology in services for people with learning difficulties. *Behavioral Psychotherapy, 17,* 101–117.

Halpern, A. S., & Fuhrer, M. J. (1984). Assessment and training of job-related social competence for mentally retarded adolescents and adults. *Functional assessment in rehabilitation* (pp. 145–157). Baltimore, MD: Paul H. Brookes Publishing.

Nicoholi, A. M. (1978). *The Harvard guide to modern psychiatry.* Cambridge, MA: Harvard University Press.

BIOFEEDBACK. The use of auditory and/or visual signals provided in response to neuromuscular or autonomic activity, to allow persons to gain more voluntary control over such physiological functions. *Usage Notes and Comments:* The use of biofeedback presumes that the person is volitionally involved in the process of learning rather than merely a physiological respondent. There are a number of theoretical models that have been used to define and explain biofeedback, including learning theory and cybernetics. A learning theory of biofeedback focuses on principles of instrumental learning of physiological activity. The cybernetic model provides an information-processing explanation of biofeedback. For example, biofeedback may be conceptualized as providing environmental cues that can result in learning, dependent on client motivation and attention.

References/Recommended Readings

Basmajian, J. V. (1983). Introduction: Principles and background. In J. V. Basmajian (Ed.), *Biofeedback: Principles and practice for clinicians* (2nd ed.) (pp. 1–5). Baltimore: Williams & Wilkins.

Brucker, B. S. (1980). Biofeedback and rehabilitation. In L. P. Ince (Ed.), *Behavioral psychology in rehabilitation medicine: Clinical applications*. Baltimore: Williams & Wilkins.

Schwartz, M. S. & Associates (1987). *Biofeedback: A practitioner's guide*. New York: Guilford Press.

Shellenberger, R., & Green, J. A. (1986). *From the ghost in the box to successful biofeedback training*. Greely, Colorado: Health Psychology Publications.

BODY IMAGE THEORY. The application of psychoanalytic or psychoanalytically derived principles to explain the development of the concept of, and set of attitudes toward, oneself as a bodily entity. *Usage Notes and Comments:* Fisher (1990) has summarized current research dealing with the body as a psychological object into nine primary topical areas of inquiry. These include (a) perception and evaluation of one's own body appearance; (b) accuracy of perception of one's body size; (c) accuracy of perception of one's body sensations; (d) ability to judge the spatial position of one's body; (e) feelings about the definiteness and protective value of the body boundaries; (f) distortions in body sensations and experiences associated with psychopathology and brain damage; (g) responses to body damage, loss of parts, and surgery; (g) response to various procedures designed to camouflage the body or somehow to "improve" it; and, (h) attitudes and feelings pertinent to the sexual identity of one's body. Fisher (1990) states there has been little communication among those researching these topics with each theorist tending to develop his or her own theoretical mini-models and modes of measurement. Research has demonstrated that body image is not a unidimensional construct and that a conceptualization of body image that seeks to compress it into a few narrow categories is no longer defensible. (*See Also:* Self-concept; Self-esteem.)

References/Recommended Readings

Cleveland, S. E. (1960). Body image changes associated with personality reorganization. *Journal of Consulting Psychology, 24,* 256–261.

English, R. W. (1977). The application of personality theory to explain psychological reactions to physical disability. In R. P. Marinelli & A. E. Dell Orto (Eds.), *The psychological and social impact of physical disability* (pp. 90–129). New York: Springer Publishing Co.

Fisher, S. (1990). The evaluation of psychological concepts about the body. In T. F. Cash & T. Prozinsky (Eds.), *Body images: Development, deviance, and change* (pp. 3–20). New York: Guilford Press.

McDaniel, J. W. (1969). *Physical disability and human behavior.* New York: Pergamon Press.

Wapner, S., & Warner, H. (Eds.) (1965). *The body percept.* New York: Random House.

BURNOUT. The state of emotional and physical fatigue experienced by individuals who have incurred excessive psychological demands in their roles of helping other people. *Usage Notes and Comments:* Professionals in human service occupations are often at risk for burnout as their work is emotionally involving, and work outcomes can be influenced by many factors beyond the control of the professional. Similarly, family members who assume primary caregiver roles with a member who has sustained a debilitating disease or injury may also experience burnout. In a widely recognized conceptualization of burnout, Maslach and Jackson (1981) theorized three components: (1) emotional exhaustion, (2) depersonalization, and, (3) feelings of low personal accomplishment. Emotional exhaustion is defined as the degree of fatigue due to excessive emotional demands. Depersonalization refers to the tendency of professionals to detach from feelings of concern for clientele moving toward a regard for clients as impersonal objects. Lack of personal accomplishment is defined as the dearth of motivation and sense of inefficacy resulting from prolonged exposure to discouraging and demanding work conditions.

It is imperative to note that many rehabilitation professionals report burnout experiences, and the syndrome appears to be evident across disciplines. Length of service in a rehabilitation unit has been linked to greater emotional exhaustion and depersonalization among nurses (Sherwin et al., 1992). Social workers in rehabilitation units report greater burnout than counterparts in other work settings (Stav & Florian, 1986). It also appears that certain personal and environmental conditions can buffer some professionals against burnout. Higher levels of burnout over time have been related to greater employee dissatisfaction, turnover, and voluntary leaving.

References/Recommended Readings

Maslach, C., & Jackson, S. E. (1981). The measurement of experienced burnout. *Journal of Occupational Behavior, 2,* 99–113.

Pines, A., & Aronson, E. (1988). *Career burnout: Causes and cures.* New York: Free Press.

Sherwin, E. D., Elliott, T. R., Rybarcyzk, B., Frank, R., Hanson, S., & Hoffman, J. (1992). Negotiating the reality of caregiving: Hope, burnout, and nursing. *Journal of Social and Clinical Psychology, 11,* 129–139.

Stav, A., & Florian, V. (1986). Burnout among social workers working with physically disabled persons and bereaved families. *Journal of Social Service Research, 10*(1), 81–94.

Ursprung, A. W. (1986). Burnout in the human services: A review of the literature. *Rehabilitation Counseling Bulletin, 29*(3), 190–199.

CAREGIVER BURDEN. Negative consequences of caring for individuals who have chronic disabilities typically occuring when demands of care exceed the caregiver's coping resources. *Usage Notes and Comments:* There has been a great deal of variability in how caregiver burden has been conceptualized and measured, and a lack of theoretical focus has made it difficult to interpret results across studies of this concept (Ravens, Siegel, & Sudit, 1989). Caregiver burden can be measured in two general ways—objective burden and subjective burden. *Objective burden* includes observable changes in the personality and behavior of the person receiving care, as well as environmental changes for the caregiver such as financial strain, changes in routine, changes in living conditions, and changes in social activities. *Subjective burden* is the caregiver's negative reaction resulting from the presence of objective burden.

Many studies have attempted to use objective burden (e.g., patient variables) to predict subjective burden and outcome. However, among spouse caregivers of persons with head injuries, for example, there was no simple relationship between the objective severity of the injury and the caregiver's experience (Brooks, Campsie, Symington, Beattie, & McKinlay, 1987). Cognitive and physical impairments were also not consistent predictors of their experience. Emotional and characterological impairments associated with brain dysfunction were, however, found to be consistently associated with subjective burden and negative physical and mental health outcomes. These mixed results suggest that caregiver burden is not directly associated with objective events or patient characteristics.

References/Recommended Readings

Brooks, N., Campsie, L., Symington, C., Beattie, A., & McKinlay, W. (1987). The effects of severe head injury on patient and relative within seven years of injury. *Journal of Head Trauma Rehabilitation, 2,* 1–13.

Chwalisz, K. (1992). Perceived stress and caregiver burden after brain injury: A theoretical integration. *Rehabilitation Psychology, 37*(3), 189–203.

Ravens, V. H., Siegel, K., & Sudit, H. (1989). Psychological impact of caregiving on the care provider: A critical review of the extant research. *Journal of Applied Social Sciences, 13,* 40–79.

CASE MANAGEMENT. Coordination and integration of services and other resources designed to enhance the functioning of a client or group of clients. *Usage Notes and Comments:* Case management is typically performed by one individual on behalf of another although it may be undertaken by a team and be targeted to couples or families. Any or all of the following activities may be included in this service: casefinding, needs assessment, planning and arranging delivery of services, follow-up of clients/services, and reassessment.

Case management has expanded into a range of health, mental health, and social service settings over the past two decades. Case managers are typically social workers, rehabilitation counselors, or nurses employed by hospitals or community-based programs. A growing number of private practitioners are offering case management services as well.

There are a range of possible outcomes that may motivate the provision of case management services, including improved quality of life, greater efficiency of service delivery, and cost containment.

References/Recommended Readings

Barker, R. L. (1987). *The social work dictionary*. Silver Spring, MD: National Association of Social Workers.

Kaplan, K. O. (1990). Recent trends in case management. In A. Minahan (Editor-in-Chief) *Encyclopedia of social work* (18th ed., 1990 supplement). Silver Spring, MD: National Association of Social Workers.

Maddox, G. L. (Ed.). (1987). *The encyclopedia of aging*. New York: Springer Publishing Co.

COMPENSATORY MODEL. A theory which hypothesizes that persons with physical disabilities are likely to emphasize positive attributes over which they have some control to compensate for perceived deficits. *Usage Notes and Comments:* This model suggests that persons with physical disabilities are likely to strive forcefully (e.g., appear attractive and fashionably dressed) to ameliorate the social consequences of apparent difference from the norm. The compensatory model focuses on the motivations behind impression management. (See Also: Negotiated-Outcomes Model.)

Recommended Reading

Kleck, R. E., & Strenta, A. (1980). Perceptions of the impact of negatively valued physical characteristics on social interaction. *Journal of Personality and Social Psychology, 39*, 861–873.

CONTAINMENT. The limiting of the experience of loss to functions that are directly affected by a disability or other types of loss or misfortune. (*See Also: Spread.*)

Recommended Reading

Dembo, T., Leviton, G.L., & Wright, B.A. (1975). Adjustment to misfortune: A problem of social psychological rehabilitation. *Rehabilitation Psychology, 22,* 1–100. (Originally published in *Artificial Limbs,* (1956), 4–62).
Wright, B.A. (1983). *Physical disability: A psychosocial approach* (2nd ed.). New York: Harper & Row.

CONTINGENCY CONTRACT. A mutual agreement, frequently in writing, between the treating practitioner and the client in which the individual agrees to treatment and the targeted behaviors or targeted behaviors, the reinforcers, and the contingencies are specified. *Usage Notes and Comments:* To avoid coercion in a contingency contract, both parties mutually agree to its tenets. Research has demonstrated that continuation in treatment programs seems to be enhanced when such contracts are employed, particularly when clients participate in the development and implementation of the contingencies and the agreements include consequences for failing to meet the conditions. (*See Also:* Behavior Analysis; Behavior Modification.)

Recommended Reading

Kazdin, A. E. (1975). Recent advances in token economy research. In Hersen, M., Eisler, R. M., & Miller, P. M. (Eds.), *Progress in behavior modification.* New York: Academic Press.

COPING. The cognitive and behavioral efforts to reduce, master, or tolerate stressful situations and the emotional reactions that accompany them. *Notes and Comments:* Recent theory and research suggest that coping includes thoughts and actions that can be directed both at altering the troubled person–environment transaction (problem-focused coping) and regulating distressing emotions (emotion-focused coping). Coping behavior has been widely regarded as playing a central role in the process of adapting to physical illness through its linkage to the concept of stress, impaired functioning, health, morale and accomplishment (Lazarus, 1966).

There are four general ways in which coping has been theorized to affect health outcomes (Holroyd & Lazarus, 1982). First, coping influences the frequency, intensity, and patterning of neuroendocrine stress responses. Coping may mediate this relationship by preventing stressful events from occurring or by enabling the individual to avoid or resolve difficulties that do occur. Emotion-focused coping also can either moderate stress emotions and associated physiological mobilization or intensify and prolong the stress emotions that occur in response to even minor difficulties.

Second, coping styles can influence health outcomes though the manner in which they influence illness behavior (i.e., reporting symptoms and/or seeking treatment) or actual physiological symptoms that serve coping functions. Illness behavior may serve stabilizing functions in conflicting families (Minuchin, Rosman, & Baker, 1978) or be maintained by reinforcements produced (Whitehead, Fedoravicius, Blackwell, & Wooley, 1979).

Third, coping styles may contribute to disease because they involve changes in health behaviors that expose the individual to injurious agents such as alcohol, tobacco smoke, or allergens. For example, people at risk for coronary heart disease may increase their smoking in response to stress (Horowitz et al., 1979), or persons with peptic duodenal ulcers may increase their consumption of alcohol in response to work stress (Weisman, 1956). Finally, the way the individual copes with the threat of acute illness (Moos, 1982) or with the demands of chronic illness (Cohen & Lazarus, 1979; Shontz, 1982) can be an important determinant of the course of an illness and of the medical care received (Jones, Kinsman, Dirks, & Dahlem, 1979). (*See Also:* Acceptance of Disability; Accommodation; Adjustment; Succumbing Framework.)

References/Recommended Readings

Cohen, F., & Lazarus, R. S. (1979). Coping with stresses of illness. In G. C. Stone, F. Cohen, & N. E. Adler (Eds.), *Health psychology: A handbook: Theories, applications, and challenges of a psychological approach to the health care system.* San Francisco: Jossey-Bass.

Folkman, S., Lazarus, R. S., Pimley, S., & Novacek, J. (1987). Age differences in stress and coping processes. *Psychology and Aging, 2,* 171–184.

Holroyd, K. A., & Lazarus, R. S. (1982). Stress, coping, and somatic adaptation. In Goldberger, L. & Breznitz, S. (Eds.), *Handbook of stress: Theoretical and clinical aspects.* New York: The Free Press.

Horowitz, M. J., Hulley, S., Alvarez, W., Reynolds, A. M., Benfari, R., Blair, S., Borhani, N., & Simon, N. (1979). Life events, risk factors, and coronary disease. *Psychosomatics, 20,* 586–592.

Jones, N. F., Kinsman, R. A., Dirks, J. F., & Dahlem, N. W. (1979). Psychological contributions to chronicity in asthma: Patient response styles influencing medical treatment and its outcome. *Medical Care, 17,* 1103–1118.

Lazarus, R. S. (1966). *Psychological stress and the coping process.* New York: McGraw-Hill.

Lazarus, R. S., & Folkman, S. (1984). *Stress, appraisal, and coping.* New York: Springer Publishing Co.

Minuchin, S., Rosman, B. L., & Baker, L. (1978). *Psychosomatic families.* Cambridge: Harvard University Press.

Moos, R. (1982). Coping with acute health crises. In T. Millon, C. Green, & R. Meagher (Eds.), *Handbook of clinical health psychology.* New York: Plenum.

Shontz, F. (1982). Adaptation to chronic illness and disability. In T. Millon, C. Green & Meagher (Eds.), *Handbook of clinical health psychology.* New York: Plenum.

Weisman, A. (1956). A study of the psychodynamics of duodenal ulcer exacerbations with special reference to treatment and the problem of specificity. *Psychosomatic Medicine, 18,* 2–42.

Whitehead, W. E., Fedoravicus, R. S., Blackwell, B., & Wooley, S. (1979). A behavioral conceptualization of psychosomatic illness: Psychosomatic symptoms as learned responses. In J. R. McNamara (Ed.), *Behavioral approaches to medicine: Application and analysis.* New York: Plenum.

COPING VERSUS SUCCUMBING FRAME- WORKS. Frameworks that represent different ways of viewing the significance of disability with the succumbing framework highlighting the negative aspects of disablement, and the coping framework focusing on abilities in terms of their intrinsic or asset value. *Usage Notes and Comments:* Although the following discussion considers coping versus succumbing frameworks as pure cases, in real life, vacillation between them or mixed forms can occur. "The succumbing framework highlights the negative impact of disablement, giving scant attention to the challenge for change and meaningful adaptation. Prevention and cure are seen as the only valid answers. Satisfactions and assets are minimized or ignored. The emphasis is on the heartache, or the loss, on what the person cannot do. Such a state is viewed as pitiful and tragic. The person as an individual with a highly differentiated and unique personality is lost. The coping framework, on the other hand, orients the perceiver to appreciate the abilities of the person in terms of their intrinsic or asset value. People with disabilities are regarded as having an active role in their own lives and in the community, not as being passively devastated by difficulties. The problem of managing difficulties has a double focus. One is geared toward environmental change; that is, changing those alterable conditions that add to the person's handicap such as architectural barriers, discriminatory practices, lack of employment opportunities, family problems, and inadequate education, housing, and transportation. The second focus concentrates on change in the person through medical procedures that reduce the disability, education and training that lead to new skills, and value restructuring that allows the person to accept the [disability] as nondevaluating. As for the suffering associated with disability, the coping framework is oriented toward seeking solutions and discovering satisfactions in living. Moreover, it recognizes the disability as only one aspect of a multifaceted life that includes gratifications as well as grievances, abilities as well as disabilities. It should be understood that concentrating on the coping possibilities does not imply glossing over the difficulties themselves" (Wright, 1983, p. 194).

The coping framework describes basic features of a constructive view of life with a disability, whereas the succumbing framework orients the viewer to devaluation and maladaptation. The two frameworks are perceptual in nature and apply to all people whether or not the person has a disability. The different perceptual orientations of these frameworks lead to major consequences for how we think about and act on wide-ranging disability related matters, such as the adjustment process, interpersonal relations, role-playing, fundraising, health-care messages, language usage, and civil rights legislation.

References/Recommended Readings

Adler, A. B., Wright, B. A. & Ulichny, G. R. (1991). Fundraising portrayals of people with disabilities: Donations and attitudes. *Rehabilitation Psychology, 36,* 233–242.

Wright, B. A. (1975). The coping framework and attitude change: A guide to constructive role-playing. *Rehabilitation Psychology, 4,* 177–183.

Wright, B. A. (1983). Physical disability—a psychosocial approach (2nd ed). Chapter 9. New York: Harper & Row.

CRISIS THEORY. A conceptual framework that views the onset of disability or illness as a crisis-inducing event. *Usage Notes and Comments:* Several crisis theorists have postulated a series of stages one must pass through in a linear fashion in dealing with the crisis experience (e.g., Cohn, 1961; Davis, 1963; Fink, 1967). In contrast, Shontz (1965) describes adjustment to crisis as a series of approach–avoidance cycles. Each cycle occurs rapidly in the early stages of reaction to disability and later, once adjustment is achieved, the cyclic nature of the process becomes virtually unnoticeable. Fordyce (1982) describes a process of crisis as occurring within the context of a learning theory approach. (*See Also:* Developmental Stage Models.)

References/Recommended Readings

Cohn, N. (1961). Understanding the process of adjustment to disability. *Journal of Rehabilitation, 27,* 16–18.

Davis, F. (1963). Passage through crisis: Polio victims and their families. New York: Bobbs-Merrill.

English, R. W. (1977). The application of personality theory to explain psychological reactions to physical disabilities (pp. 909–129). In R. P. Marinelli & A. E. Dell Orto (Eds.), *The psychological and social impact of physical disability.* New York: Springer Publishing Co.

Fink, S. L. (1967). Crisis and motivation: A theoretical model. *Archives of Physical Medicine and Rehabilitation, 48,* 592–597.

Fordyce, W. (1982). Psychological assessment and management. In F. Kottke, G. Stillwell, & J. Lehman (Eds.), *Krusen's handbook of physical medicine and rehabilitation* (3rd ed.) (pp. 124–150). Philadelphia: W. B. Saunders.

Shontz, F. C. (1975). *The psychological aspects of physical illness and disability.* New York: Macmillan.

DEVALUATION. A process through which some view persons with disabilities as lacking something of importance, with the result that their worth is devalued and their being held in lower social esteem. *Usage Notes and Comments:* Devaluation is expressed in various ways. It may manifest as a patronizing attitude, whereby a person with a disability is treated in a pitying way, or an object of charity. Alternatively, devaluation can be seen as an attitude of aversion toward a person with a disability. Sometimes the experience of persons with disabilities may contribute to their own self-devaluation, or lessened feelings of self-worth.

The term devaluation has been used in disability literature for at least 30 years. Wright (1960) discusses this concept, and elaborates on how an inferior social-status position conferred by society on persons with disabilities might impact their ability to cope effectively with life demands. More recently, Wolfensberger (Thomas & Wolfensberger, 1982) introduced the concept of "normalization" as a way to overcome the devaluation of persons with disabilities and encouraged the adoption of measures that would lead to a more positive view of each person. For example, most people can identify with a residential program for individuals with disabilities that operates in a typical home or apartment setting in the community, because most people themselves reside in such settings. Wolfensberger thus introduced the concept of normalization of the experiences of persons with disabilities to lessen the devaluation by society that they may experience. Additionally, he discussed the role of advocacy in achieving normalization (Wolfensberger, 1972, Wolfensberger & Zauha, 1973). (*See Also:* Normalization, Normalization Principle; Stigma.)

References/Recommended Readings

Goffman, E. (1963). *Stigma: Notes on the management of spoiled identity*. Englewood Cliffs, NJ: Prentice-Hall, Inc.

Thomas, S., & Wolfensberger, W. (1982). The importance of social imagery to interpreting societally devalued people to the public. *Rehabilitation Literature, 43,* 11–12, 356–358.

Wolfensberger, W. (1972). *Citizen advocacy*. Washington, DC: The President's Committee on Mental Retardation.

Wolfensberger, W., & Zauha, H. (1973). *Citizen advocacy of protective services for the impaired and handicapped*. Toronto, Canada: National Institute on Mental Retardation.

Wright, B. A. (1960). *Physical disability—A psychological approach*. New York: Harper & Brothers.

Wright, G. N. (1980). *Total rehabilitation*. Boston: Little, Brown and Co.

DEVELOPMENTAL STAGE MODELS. A conceptualization of the adjustment process in which stages are proposed in an attempt to describe characteristic patterns of behavior. *Usage Notes and Comments:* Many personality theorists have examined a series of stages in which development is thought to occur in order to increase their understanding of psychopathology. Much support has been found for the premise that development proceeds by steps rather than smoothly (Erikson, 1968; Havighurst, 1948; Jung, 1933). Throughout these periods of development, certain achievements are expected to provide for the emergence of a normal and healthy identity. Each step is believed to contribute uniquely to the developing ego. Normal development is felt to be the result of mastery of the tasks of each life stage prior to passage to the subsequent stage. The hypothesis that the relatively specific effects of an event on a particular life stage will result in equally specific vulnerabilities and, hence, unique psychopathology constitutes the basis of developmental approaches. Moreover, it is implicit in such theories that minimal conditions must exist for the individual to satisfactorily meet the demands of each of these steps. Finally, the ease of passage through later steps is thought to be facilitated by the degree of success in completing preceding stages (Erickson, 1963).

Also implicit in developmental theories is the requirements

for physical, emotional, and cognitive tools with which to meet all the demands that any step may impose. Clearly, to the extent that disabling conditions may diminish the physical, emotional, or cognitive capabilities of the individual, they might be expected to disrupt the smooth transition through the current stage. In addition, disabling conditions may impair the capacity of the environment and significant others to provide optimal conditions for a given life stage.

The most immediate effect of a disabling condition is the obstruction of activities normal for that life stage. It should be borne in mind that the tasks of each life stage are also the major activities of that step. For example, if the major task for the school-age child is the development of academic competence, it is not only an important quality for later life, but the major activity of the child. Similarly, if a task for an adult is bearing and rearing children, that activity is of utmost signficance, regardless of subsequent life stages.

A further consequence of the disrupting influence of disability on development is failure to acquire essential qualities required for a healthy and complete ego. Moreover, as later development depends, in part, on adequate acquisition of living skills of prior stages, stage theorists purport that the individual may be handicapped in approaching all subsequent challenges of life. (*See Also:* Accommodation; Adjustment; Crisis Theory; Interpersonal Theory; Loss Resolution; Somatopsychology.)

References/Recommended Readings

Eisenberg, M. G., Sutkin, L. C., & Jansen, M. A. (Eds.) (1984). *Chronic illness and disability through the lifespan: Effects on self and family.* New York: Springer Publishing Co.

Erickson, E. H. (1968). *Identity and crisis.* New York: Norton.

Havinghurst, R. (1948). *Developmental tasks and education* (3rd ed.). New York: David McKay.

Jung, C. G. (1933). *Modern man in search of a soul.* New York: Harcourt, Brace & World.

DISABILITY.   An impairment resulting in any restriction or lack of ability to perform an activity in the manner, or in the range, ordinarily expected. *Usage Notes and Comments:* Disability is defined as meaning a physical or mental impairment that substantially limits one or more major life activities, a record of such an impairment, or being regarded as having such an impairment. This is the same definition of the term as it appears in section 504 of the Rehabilitation Act of 1973, the Fair Housing Act Amendments, and the Air Carriers Access Act.

The definitions of disability mean that, apart from its underlying origins and ultimate effects, disability is a limitation in life activities, such as working or living independently, caused by a wide variety of impairments or other chronic conditions, such as blindness, arthritis, mental retardation, or panic disorders. Disability is defined in terms of many areas of functioning, such as physical (e.g., walking), emotional (e.g., interpersonal relationships), and mental (e.g., problem solving). Although acute conditions do cause disabilities, the existing literature on disability focuses almost exclusively on limitations related to chronic conditions. The rationale for this focus is that acute conditions, although having a potentially substantial effect, do not usually require prolonged behavioral or social adaptation. Definitional differences aside, the focus of many disability studies is on describing the various types of limitations caused by chronic health conditions, as opposed to the conditions themselves. Rather than treating disability as a disorder in need of correction, this approach considers the functional capacity and needs of the individuals involved, attempting to provide reasonable accommodations in accord with those capacities and needs. This nonmedical perspective on disability has gained wide acceptance in the professional community, as have the clear benefits of treatment, health promotion, disease prevention, and the use of such technology as medical device implants and assistive devices. (*See Also:* Activity Limitation; Americans with Disabilities Act of 1990; Disablement, Levels of; Functional Limitation; Handicap; Impairment; Major Life Activities; Qualified Handicapped Person; Reasonable Accommodation; Secondary Gain; Work Disability.)

References/Recommended Readings

Haber, L. D. (1990). Issues in the definition of disability and the use of disability survey data. In D. B. Levine, M. Zitter,

& L. Ingram (Eds.), *Disability statistics: An assessment report of a workshop*. Washington, DC: Committee on National Statistics, Commission on Behavioral and Social Sciences and Education, National Research Council, National Academy Press.

World Health Organization (1980). *International classification of impairments, disabilities, and handicaps*. Geneva: World Health Organization.

Wright, B. A. (1983). Circumscribing the problem. *Physical disability—A psychosocial approach*. (2nd ed.), (pp 1–12). Philadelphia: Harper & Row.

DISABLEMENT, LEVELS OF. A generic term referring to any experience identified variously by the terms impairment, disability or handicap. *Usage Notes and Comments:* Based on World Health Organization's (1980) definitions, when the impairment interferes with the performance of a task, it is termed a disability. When the disability interferes with the performance of a role, it then becomes regarded as a handicap. For example, deficiencies in vascular circulation (impairment) from diabetes eventually result in a lower leg amputation. Consequent changes in ambulation or gait (a disability) may result, in turn, in the loss of a role performance, such as a manual labor occupation, which consequently becomes regarded as a handicap to this individual.

Nagi (1976) presented a similar schema in his description of levels of disablement. Graphically, his model is represented below:

Pathology→Impairment→Functional Limitations→Disability

In this model, the first two stages are similar to those proposed by the World Health Organization (WHO), with functional limitations reflecting performance at the individual level. For Nagi, however, disability encompasses both role performance deficiencies and those deficiencies that result from individual characteristics. Granger (1984) has integrated these two views into a framework that stresses the importance of function as a central concern in rehabilitation. He also differentiates the emphasis on function from the usual medical model that focuses on cure.

Two classes of variables have recently been added to the Nagi model (Institute of Medicine, 1991), including factors that impinge on the processes occurring at any stage of the disablement process. The first class is risk factors that are biological, environmental (social and physical), and lifestyle or behavioral characteristics that are associated with health. The second class includes quality of life factors such as standard of living, life satisfaction, employment, and housing, which are clearly related to the social circumstances of the individual. (*See Also:* Americans with Disabilities Act of 1990; Disability; Functional Limitation; Handicap; Impairment.)

References/Recommended Readings

Granger, C. V. (1984). A conceptual model of functional assessment. In C. V. Granger & G. E. Gresham (Eds.), *Functional assessment in rehabilitation medicine* (pp. 14–25). Baltimore: Williams & Wilkins.

Institute of Medicine. (1991). *Disability in America.* Washington, DC: National Academy Press.

Keith, R. A. (1993). The role of theory in rehabilitation assessment, treatment and outcomes. In R. L. Glueckauf, L. B. Sechrest, G. R. Bond, & E. McDonel (Eds.), *Improving rehabilitation assessment practice: Issues and new directions.* Newbury Park, CA: Sage.

Nagi, S. Z. (1976). An epidemiology of disability among adults in the United States. *Milbank Memorial Fund Quarterly/Health and Society, 54,* 439–467.

Nagi, S. Z. (1991). Disability concepts revisited: Implications for prevention. In Institute of Medicine. *Disability in America* (pp. 309-327). Washington, DC: National Academy Press.

World Health Organization (1980). *International classification of impairments, disabilities, and handicaps.* Geneva: World Health Organization.

DISABLING LANGUAGE.   See Nonhandicapping Language.

EFFICACY EXPECTATIONS.   The belief that one can successfully execute the behaviors required to produce a

particular outcome. *Usage Notes and Comments:* Another term used synonymously with "efficacy expectations" is self-efficacy expectations. Efficacy expectations are one aspect of self-efficacy theory, which has been schematically described by Bandura (1977) as follows:

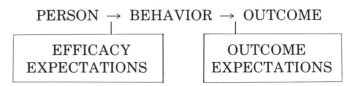

PERSON → BEHAVIOR → OUTCOME

| EFFICACY EXPECTATIONS | OUTCOME EXPECTATIONS |

Efficacy expectations are conceptualized as being different from outcome expectations. Outcome expectations are defined as a person's estimate that a given behavior will lead to certain outcomes. For example, a person will be more likely to attempt to walk using parallel bars in physical therapy for the first time if the person believes that the attempt will be successful. One will be more likely to attempt this new activity if the person believes that walking with the use of parallel bars will ultimately generalize to improved ambulation outside of the physical therapy area (outcome expectation). Bandura emphasizes the role of efficacy expectations rather than outcome expectations in self-efficacy theory.

Efficacy expectations are believed to determine whether coping behavior will be initiated, how much effort will be expended, and how long coping behaviors will be maintained in the face of barriers. Characteristics of efficacy expectations that impact prediction of performance include: magnitude, generality, and strength. Level of task difficulty affects the magnitude of the efficacy expectation needed to initiate a behavior. As an illustration, one may believe in his or her ability to stand independently from the wheelchair but not believe in one's ability to ambulate using the parallel bars, a more difficult task. Efficacy expectations can differ in generality. Mastery of one challenging situation may enhance efficacy expectations in another situation. For example, the person who ambulated successfully in the parallel bars may then expect success in attempting other challenges in the prescribed rehabilitation program and, consequently, be more willing to take risks. Expectations can also vary in strength. The stronger the person's beliefs of mastery, the more willing the person is to persist in coping attempts despite set backs or obstacles that may occur.

References/Recommended Readings

Bandura, A. (1977). Self-efficacy: Toward a unifying theory of behavioral change. Psychological Review, *84,* 191–125.

Bandura, A. (1982). Self-efficacy mechanism in human agency. *American Psychologist, 37,* 122–147.

Maddux, J. E. (1991). Self-efficacy. In C. R. Snyder, & D. R. Donelson (Eds.), *Handbook of social and clinical psychology* (pp. 57–78). New York: Pergamon Press.

EMPOWERMENT. Psychosocial intervention strategies that enhance feelings of self-efficacy, increase the sense of personal control, and instill skills and capabilities essential for self-direction and community participation. *Usage Notes and Comments:* Empowerment refers both to a process and a desirable outcome; that is, empowered individuals possess and demonstrate the above-described qualities. The term empowerment (or sometimes self-empowerment) originated in community action research in the 1970s, referring generally to the capacity of disenfranchised citizens to become active participants in matters that affect their lives. A prominent researcher in the area, Rappaport (1981), defined empowerment as an attempt to "enhance the possibilities for people to control their own lives" (p. 15).

Checkoway and Norsman (1986) described empowerment as a process in which persons with disabilities organize to provide mutual support in the struggle for independence and the right to live normal lives in the mainstream of society. Hahn (1991) proposed that insights developed and skills acquired from experience with disability can result in a positive sense of identity for persons with disabilities and become the foundation for a sense of empowerment. Consistent with his view that people with disabilities constitute an oppressed group that is the victim of injustice, Condeluchi (1989) proposed three stages in the empowerment process: (a) raise consciousness, increase sensitivity and awareness of the general public, and foster desire for change; (b) locate a target responsible for the situation, which can be a law, regulation, or group of people; and, (c) select a strategy that is matched to the particular target identified.

From the various definitions and discussions originating in the professional literature of rehabilitation and community psychology, it is possible to establish the general parameters and primary facets of empowerment. First, empowerment involves both individual traits and social interaction. Second, empowerment subsumes both attitudes and capabilities. Third, components of empowerment include: assertiveness, creativity, decision-making skills, independence, interdependence, positive sense of identity as a person with a disability, problem-solving skills, self-actualization, self-advocacy, self-respect, self-responsibility, sense of competence, sense of political purpose, and sense of social responsibility. (*See Also:* Independent Living.)

References/Recommended Readings

Checkoway, B., & Norsman, A. (1986). Empowering citizens with disabilities. *Community Development Journal, 21*(4), 270–277.

Condeluchi, A. (1989). The stages of empowerment. *JMA Bulletin,* 1(2), 11–14.

Hahn, H. (1991). Alternative views of empowerment: Social services and civil rights. *Journal of Rehabilitation, 57*(4), 17–19.

Rappaport, J. (1981). In praise of paradox: A social policy of empowerment over prevention. *American Journal of Community Psychology, 9,* 1–25.

Ward, M. J. (1988). The many facets of self-determination. *Transition Summary, 5,* 2–3.

ENLARGING THE SCOPE OF VALUES.

Appreciation for the values, capabilities, and activities that are still accessible to an individual irrespective of disability. *Usage Notes and Comments:* Enlarging the scope of values is one type of value change underlying the acceptance of loss and acceptance of disability, as conceptualized by Dembo, Leviton, and Wright (1956; see also, Wright, 1983). The initial reaction to disability can often include a period of mourning, which in turn involves emotional responses such as anger, pervasive despair, or depression. A mourning response is often regarded as a period during which the person comes to terms with the loss. A value change that may occur in accepting the loss has been referred to as enlarging the scope of values. Wright (1983) regards this as "emotionally appreciating the existence of values in addition to the one(s) lost" (p. 163). She discusses the following processes as being important in overcoming mourning: comparison of one's state with other states, arousal of dormant values, satiation, and mastering the activities of daily living. (*See Also:* Interpersonal Theory; Mourning, Requirement of; Somatopsychology.)

References

Dembo, T., Leviton, G. L. & Wright, B. A. (1956). Adjustment to misfortune—A problem of social psychological rehabilitation. *Artificial Limbs, 3*(2), 4–62.

Wright, B. A. (1983). *Physical disability—A psychosocial approach* (2nd ed.). New York: Harper & Row.

EXPECTATION DISCREPANCY.

A discrepancy between the expectations held by an observer who encounters a person with a disability and the actual observations of the person and his or her characteristics, statements, or behavior. *Usage Notes and Comments:* Expectation discrepancy is a concept developed in somatopsychology or interpersonal theory (see Wright, 1983) to explain common reactions of observers when encountering individuals with disabilities. When expectations are more negative than observed reality, the existence of an expectation discrepancy may be evident in the reaction of "surprise" on the part of the observer. For example, an observer may be surprised on first meeting a person with cerebral palsy who appears to be "happy" rather than distressed, despite the circumstances of the disability; to be employed in a professional occupation, married, and apparently living a full and productive life; and as being able to perform many activities that the observer might have expected to be difficult, if not impossible. As another example, an observer may be surprised to learn that an accomplished musician is blind, not initially expecting that a person who is blind would be capable of that level of achievement.

Wright (1983) discussed several mechanisms or conditions that would appear to underlie expectation discrepancies: (a) *spread*—the tendency to overgeneralize the effects of a disability as limiting a person in functions that are actually unrelated to the disability; (b) *position of an observer as an outsider*—the lack of experience of the observer with the disability and, thus, not having the opportunities to learn or discover ways to cope with challenges presented; and (c) *self-aggrandizing requirement of mourning*—the need to feel superior to a person considered "unfortunate" because of a disability, resulting in an expectation that the person "mourn" his or her situation in order to preserve and enhance the superior status of the nondisabled observer. In addition, a *wish for improvement* may be seen as underlying unrealistic expectations that an illness or disability will improve or that a new treatment will be successful, resulting in expectations that are discrepant with observed reality.

Wright (1983) notes three different mechanisms by which expectation discrepancies may be revised: (a) *expectation revision*—revising the original expectations so that they become more consistent with observations; (b) *altering the apparent reality*—concluding that the apparent observations are inaccurate and that the person is not managing nearly as well as it appears; and (c) *abnormalization*—ascribing supernatural powers to the individual to explain observed behavior or accomplishments as, for example, believing that people who are blind must have a "sixth sense" allowing them to perform functions believed to be impossible without sight. Expectation revision is seen as providing the most adaptive mechanism for revising expectation discrepancies. (*See Also:* Insider versus Outsider Phenomenon; Interpersonal Theory; Mourning, Requirement of; Somatopsychology; Spread.)

References/Recommended Readings

Wright, B. A. (1974). An analysis of attitudes—Dynamics and effects. *New Outlook for the Blind, 66,* 108–118.

Wright, B. A. (1983). *Physical disability—A psychosocial approach* (2nd ed.). New York: Harper & Row.

FUNCTIONAL ASSESSMENT. The measurement of activities, skills, roles, or needs in specified settings or situations, where the functional difficulties can be remediated through training or ameliorated by environmental modification. *Usage Notes and Comments:* Functional assessment instruments may measure individual capacities (what the person is capable of doing) or behaviors (what the person actually does); they should address strengths and assets, as well as limitations and deficits; and they must quantify the degree of impairment in relation to performance in a particular environmental context or situation (West Virginia Research and Training Center, 1983). Functional assessment instruments are useful in the following ways: (1) diagnosing individual rehabilitation needs and problems that may potentially be remediated through service provision, (2) justifying the service provider's decisions regarding eligibility determination and the development of the rehabilitation plan, and (3) establishing accountability by documenting the benefits of services as reflected in improvements in functioning. It is important to emphasize that the validity of this measurement approach is dependent on the domain sampling strategy; that is, the items or tasks composing the instrument must be representative of the specified behavioral domain of interest. Brown, Gordon, and Diller (1982) presented a comprehensive functional assessment model for outcome analysis and measurement in rehabilitation. A thorough historical review of the concept of functional assessment is presented by Frey (1984). Brief reviews of six exemplary functional assessment instruments are provided by Crewe (1987). (*See Also:* Activities of Daily Living; Functional Limitation.)

References

Brown, M., Gordon, W. A., & Diller, L. (1982). Functional assessment and outcome measurement: An integrative review. *Annual Review of Rehabilitation, 3,* 93–120.

Crewe, N. M. (1987). Assessment of physical functioning. In B. Bolton (Ed.), *Handbook of measurement and evaluation in rehabilitation* (2nd ed.), (pp. 235–247). Baltimore, MD: Paul H. Brookes.

Frey, W. D. (1984). Functional assessment in the '80s: A conceptual enigma, a technical challenge. In A. S. Halpern & M. J. Fuhrer (Eds.), *Functional assessment in rehabilitation* (pp. 11–43). Baltimore, MD: Paul H. Brooks.

West Virginia Research and Training Center (1983). *Tenth institute on rehabilitation issues: Functional assessment.* Dunbar, WV: Author.

FUNCTIONAL LIMITATION. A restriction or lack of ability to perform an activity that results from an impairment and may constitute a disability. *Usage Notes and Comments:* The term functional limitation derives from a conceptual model developed by Nagi (1965, 1969, 1977). Nagi's model begins with the disruption of normal body functioning, which is referred to as active pathology. Pathology can result in an impairment, which is defined as a physiological, anatomical, or psychological loss or abnormality. Limitations in activities such as walking and reasoning are the consequences of impairments. Finally, a functional limitation may constitute a disability, which is defined as an inability to perform an expected social role. For the purposes of assessment, tasks and roles are typically categorized into areas of life functioning, such as self-care, family relations, recreation, and employment.

A somewhat different, but related, definition of functional limitation resulted from a consensus conference that focused on the field of vocational rehabilitation (Indices Inc, 1978). A functional limitation is characterized by the following: (a) an inability to perform some life activity, (b) of relatively long duration, (c) caused by an interaction between an impairment and the environment, and (d) related to one's vocational potential. The Rehabilitation Amendments of 1986 and 1992 define severe disability both categorically (e.g., amputation, blindness, cerebral palsy, deafness, head injury, mental retardation, mental illness, spinal cord injury) and in terms of limitations in functional capabilities in one or more major life areas (e.g., mobility, self-care, communication, self-direction) as they relate to employability. The Coalition of Citizens with Disabilities (CCE) agrees that severe disability should be defined in terms of functional limitations in major life activities. Prevalence estimates for functional limitations in the U.S. population are summarized in Ficke (1992). (*See Also:* Activities of Daily Living; Activity

Limitation; Disability; Disablement, Levels of; Functional Assessment; Work Disability; Work Hardening.)

References

Ficke, R. C. (1992). *Digest of data on persons with disabilities.* Washington, DC: National Institute on Disability and Rehabilitation Research.

Indices, Inc. (1978). *Functional limitations: A state of the art review.* Washington, DC: Department of Health, Education, and Welfare.

Nagi, S. (1965). Some conceptual issues in disability and rehabilitation. In M. B. Sussman (Ed.), *Sociology and rehabilitation* (pp. 100–113). Washington, DC: American Sociological Association.

Nagi, S. (1969). *Disability and rehabilitation: Legal, clinical, and self-concepts and measurement.* Columbus: Ohio State University Press.

Nagi, S. (1977). The disabled and rehabilitation services: A national overview. *American Rehabilitation, 2*(5), 26–33.

FUNDAMENTAL AFFECTIVE BIAS. *See* Fundamental Negative Bias.

FUNDAMENTAL NEGATIVE BIAS. A bias that steers perception, thought, and feeling along negative lines to such a degree that positives remain hidden. *Usage Notes and Comments:* The presence of three conditions gives rise to the fundamental negative bias: "(1) if something that is observed stands out sufficiently (saliency), and (2) if, for whatever reason, it is regarded as negative (value), and (3) if its context is vague or sparse (context), then the negative value assigned to the object of observation will be a major factor in guiding perception, thinking, and feeling to fit its negative character" (Wright, 1988, p. 5). These three conditions—saliency, value, and context—also apply to something perceived as positive; that is, if something stands out that is positive and its context is sparse, then the train of thought would proceed in a positive direction. The more general bias, therefore, could be formulated as a "fundamental affective bias" in which the value of the salient object of observation with minimum context is either positive or negative. Because the fundamental negative bias has major implications for how clinical work and research are conducted and interpreted as well as for interpersonal relationships in everyday life, it is important to become sensitized to its insidious power in promoting prejudice. Counterchecks that blunt that power can then be brought to bear. Specific counterchecks depend on awareness of context issues germane to the specific situation.

A clinical example: To check the power of the fundamental bias in problem-oriented clinical settings, the sensitized clinician can "stop the action" of the mental set as soon as it is realized that the focus has been primarily on deficits. The focus can then be shifted to discovering strengths and resources in both the person and the environment. A good question to ask is, "What does the client have going for him or her?"

A research example: At least as much attention should be devoted to searching for and uncovering positive attitudes as negative attitudes toward groups who are identified by a characteristic (label) perceived as negative (e.g., disabled, poor, mentally ill), both to attenuate the negative bias and to provide a more accurate basis for improving attitudes.

Everyday life example: When meeting a stranger in whom a salient characteristic is regarded as negative, the observer can stop the action of the fundamental negative bias by "assuming nothing" further about the person. A still stronger countercheck is to substitute a mental set of "assuming abilities," thereby providing a positive context for thinking and feeling.

General countercheck: The distinction between the coping and succumbing frameworks (Wright, 1983, Chapter 9) provides a set of defining characteristics of a constructive view of disability that can be brought to the foreground as a general countercheck to devaluation stemming from the fundamental negative bias.

References/Recommended Readings

Wright, B. A. (1983). *Physical disability—A psychosocial approach* (2nd ed.). New York: Harper Collins.
Wright, B. A. (1988). Attitudes and the fundamental bias. In

H. E. Yuker (Ed.), *Attitudes toward persons with disabilities.* New York: Springer Publishing Co.

Wright, B. A. (1991). Labeling: The need for greater person-environment individuation. In C. R. Snyder & D. R. Forsyth (Eds), *Handbook of social and clinical psychology: The health perspective.* New York: Pergamon.

HANDICAP. Actual obstacles the person encounters in the pursuit of goals in real life, no matter what their source (e.g., architectural barriers (no curb cuts), legal barriers, attitudinal barriers (prejudice and discrimination). *Usage Notes and Comments:* Although the word "handicap" is defined by most as being a "disadvantage that makes achievement difficult, especially a physical disability" (Webster's Ninth New Collegiate Dictionary, 1985), it is a term that in the field of rehabilitation carries a very precise meaning and is differentiated from other terms of disablement with which it is often interchanged, those being disability and impairment. For an extended discussion of the different meanings of these three terms, the reader is referred to the definitions "Disablement, Level of" and "Qualified Handicapped Person" appearing elsewhere in this text. An example of how these terms differ from one another is perhaps best understood through an example offered by Wright:

> Certain strata of Chinese women in times past were not considered handicapped even though they could only hobble on their bound feet. Symbolizing nobility, this condition did not interfere with the functions required of such women and, therefore, presumably was not an obstacle to their goals. Although diminutive feet may be considered an impairment, they were looked upon neither as a disability nor as a handicap. An important conclusion, therefore, is that what is regarded as a disability or handicap depends upon the requirements and expectations in the situation, often culturally determined. Also important to note is that one can be handicapped without having a disability or impairment (e.g., an average height person will not be selected for the basketball team) (1983, p. 11).

(*See Also:* Americans with Disabilities Act of 1990; Disability; Disablement, Levels of; Impairment; Qualified Handicapped Person; Reasonable Accommodation.)

References/Recommended Readings

Webster's Ninth New Collegiate Dictionary (1985). Springfield, MA: Merriam-Webster.

World Health Organization (1980). *International classification of impairments, disabilities, and handicaps.* Geneva: Author.

Wright, B. A. (1983). Circumscribing the problem. *Physical disability—A psychosocial approach.* (2nd ed.) (pp. 1–12). New York: Harper & Row.

IMPAIRMENT. Any disturbance of the normal structure and functioning of the body including the systems of mental function. *Usage Notes and Comments:* An impairment is characterized by a permanent or temporary psychological, physiological, or anatomical loss or abnormality and includes the occurrence of an abnormality, defect or loss in a limb, organ, or tissue in a functional system or mechanism of the body. (*See Also:* Disablement, Levels of; Handicap; Americans with Disability Act of 1990; Disability; Qualified Handicapped Person.)

Recommended Reading

World Health Organization (WHO) (1980). *The international classification of impairments, disabilities, and handicaps—A manual of classification relating to the to the consequences of disease.* Geneva: Author.

INDEPENDENT LIVING. Control over one's life based on the choice of acceptable options that minimize reliance on other's performing everyday activities (Frieden, 1978). *Usage Notes and Comments:* The Independent Living (IL) movement represents the efforts of persons with disabilities to organize, become political, and assume greater control over their lives. The movement is based on a desire to lead the fullest life possible outside of an institution, integrated into the community, and exercising full freedom of choice. The movement began when students with severe disabilities moved out of their residential hospital settings into the community and organized their own system for delivery of survival services. Since that time, not only has the scope and number of such service delivery centers grown, but the philosophy in which they are grounded has spread throughout the rehabilitation world, challenging many of the old attitudes and policies toward treatment of the disabled.

The IL movement has its roots in a number of social movements and ideas emerging in the 1960s and 1970s: civil rights, consumerism, self-help, demoralization, and deinstitutionalization. The movement was stimulated by the 1978 amendments of the Federal Rehabilitation Act, which provided federal funds for the start-up of independent living services for persons with disabilities even if they did not have an immediate vocational goal.

The IL movement has developed programs that differ from traditional rehabilitation service delivery programs in a number of ways. These differences are in the areas of goals, methods of service delivery, and style of program management. With respect to goals, the IL programs support client self-choice rather than incorporation of the client into a set of goals established by program managers, service professionals, or funding mechanisms. Service delivery typically is not delivered by professionals but instead is carried out by peer counselors. Personal attendant care is directed by the consumer him/herself, who hires and manages his/her own attendant. Finally, IL programs are administered by persons with disabilities themselves; the managers are not professionals but consumers, as it is assumed that they know best the needs of these client populations. Service options that might be considered under independent living service programs would include: housing, including appropriate modifications of space use; health maintenance; attendant care; peer counseling; recreational activities; services to children, including the development of communication and other skills; and any preventative services to decrease future needs for rehabilitation services (Wright, 1980, p. 181). Criteria for eligibility for independent living rehabilitation under the federal regulations are: (1) the presence of severe mental or physical disabilities; (2) the presence of a severe limitation in one's ability to function independently in family and community; and, (3) a reasonable expectation that independent living rehabilitation services will significantly assist the individual to improve the ability to function independently.

Although independent living has been defined as a service delivery concept in federal regulations, it is significant as a concept unto itself (DeJong, 1979). According to the World Institute on Disability (1992), "independent living is a way of life. It is also a social and political movement that is changing both the way services are provided and the way people with disabilities fit in our society" (p. 8). (*See Also:* Empowerment; Self-Help Groups.)

References/Recommended Readings

DeJong, G. (1979). Independent living: From social movement to analytic paradigm. *Archives of Physical Medicine and Rehabilitation, 60*(10), 435–446.

Frieden, L. (1978). IL: Movement and programs. *American Rehabilitation, 3*(6), 5–7.

Frieden, L. (1979). Independent living—consumers and government join hands. *Informer, 8*(2), 5–7.

Frieden, L., & Cole, J. A. (1985). Independence: The ultimate goal of rehabilitation for spinal-cord injured persons. *The American Journal of Occupational Therapy, 39*(11), 734–739.

World Institute on Disability (1992). *Just like everyone else.* Oakland, CA: Author.

Wright, G. N. (1980). *Total rehabilitation.* Boston: Little, Brown and Co.

INSIDER VERSUS OUTSIDER PHENOMENON.

A phenomenon that defines the differing psychological positions of the "insider" with a disability (the patient, client, or actor) and the "outsider" (observer, investigator, or professional) in perceiving the impact of a disability. *Usage Notes and Comments:* The insider is the person who is *directly* affected by a disability through changes in physical functioning, attitudes, and roles. Insiders may include the actual person with the disability, family members, and close friends. The outsider is the person who is perceiving the problem of disability *indirectly*. Examples of outsiders include therapists, employers, and onlookers. Dembo (1970) concluded that there are actually two psychologies of disability; (1) the psychology of the insider, which is often emotion- and value-directed, concerned with personal, individual issues in the "here and now," and desirous of help to resolve these issues; and, (2) the psychology of the outsider, which strives to be objective and realistic and attempts to determine the "facts" by assessing the general aspects of the situation and the more probable outcomes. The latter is less concerned with the immediacy of the problems. Misunderstandings and discrepancies arise between these two positions because the outsider perceives the insider as irrational and unrealistic, whereas the insider views the outsider as insensitive and aloof. According to Dembo (1970), "traditional" psychology and the "nondisabled" community need to understand the premises and values of insiders to plan and evaluate treatment more effectively. Future research needs to focus on the differences between the insider and outsider in goals, expectations, and behavior and their implications for rehabilitation assessment and intervention (Wright, 1983). (*See Also:* Expectation Discrepancy; Interpersonal Theory; Somatopsychology.)

References/Recommended Readings

Dembo, T. (1964). Sensitivity of one person to another. *Rehabilitation Literature, 25,* 231–235.

Dembo, T. (1970). The utilization of psychological knowledge in rehabilitation. *Welfare in Review, 8,* 1–7.

Wright, B. (1983). *Physical disability—A psychosocial approach* (2nd ed.). New York: Harper and Row.

INTERPERSONAL THEORY. A conceptual framework posited by Barker and his colleagues (1946) that regards the body as a value-laden stimulus to the self and others. *Usage Notes and Comments:* Theoretical constructs that have grown out of the work of Barker and his colleagues (Barker, Wright, & Gonick, 1946; Barker, Wright, Meyerson, & Gonick, 1953; Barker & Wright, 1953; Wright, 1983) trace the self-concept and personal values back to a primary source in interpersonal relations, particularly to evaluations by others. (*See Also:* Acceptance of Disability; Developmental Stage Model; Enlarging the Scope of Values; Expectation Discrepancy; Insider versus

Outsider Phenomenon; Just World Hypothesis; Mourning, Requirement of; Overlapping Situations; Somatopsychology; Spread.)

References

Barker, R. G., & Wright, B. A. (1953). The social psychology of adjustment to physical disability (pp. 18–32). In S. F. Garrett (Ed.), *Psychological aspects of physical disability* (Rehabilitation Services Series No. 210). Washington, DC: Office of Vocational Rehabilitation, Department of HEW.

Barker, R. G., Wright, B. A., & Gonick, M. R. (1946). *Adjustment to physical handicap and illness: A survey of the social psychology of physique and disability*. New York: Social Sciences Research Council, Bulletin 55.

Barker, R. G., Wright, B. A., Meyerson, L., & Gonick, M. R. (1953). *Adjustment to physical illness and illness: A survey of the social psychology of physique and disability* (rev. ed.). New York: Social Sciences Research Council, Bulletin 55.

Wright, B. A. (1983). *Physical disability—A psychological approach*. New York: Harper and Row.

JUST WORLD HYPOTHESIS. A belief that misfortunes experienced by others do not typcially occur in a random fashion and are somehow deserved by the individual. *Usage Notes and Comments:* Lerner (Lerner, Miller, & Holmes, 1976) developed the "Just World Hypothesis" in order to offer a theoretical explanation for the counterintuitive finding that attractive persons are perceived as having greater external control over their outcomes than do unattractive persons (Cash & Begley, 1976; Wilson & Davidio, 1982). Lerner hypothesized that the misfortune or tragedy experienced by another person is perceived as random, uncontrolled, and threatening for most people. In order to reduce this feeling of threat and vulnerability, observers convince themselves that the person must have done something wrong to deserve his or her negative fate. Thus, the "Just World Hypothesis" allows one to structure another's attributions to make individuals appear as though they received the fate that they deserved. (*See Also:* Interpersonal Theory; Somatopsychology.)

References

Cash, T., & Begley, P. (1976). Internal-external control, achievement orientation, and physical attractiveness of college students. *Psychological Reports, 38,* 1205–1206.

Lerner, M., Miller, D., & Holmes, J. (1976). Deserving and the emergence of focus of justice. In L. Berkowitz & E. Walster (Eds.), *Advances in experimental social psychology* (Vol. 9). New York: Academic Press.

Wilson, M., & Davidio, J. (1982). *Effects of perceived attractiveness and feminist orientation on helping behavior.* Unpublished manuscript, DePaul University, Chicago, IL.

KINDNESS NORM. The tendency to treat and respond to persons with visible disability with overt kindness combined with covert behavioral avoidance. *Usage Notes and Comments:* In their critique of this concept, Elliott and Frank (1990) point out that several investigators have criticized assumptions and identified shortcomings of the "kindness norm" research. For example, Wright (1988) argues that the findings of many of the laboratory studies on this concept could be reinterpreted as genuine surprise from the subject that the person with the "disability" is not behaving consistent with stereotypic expectations. (*See Also:* Positivity [Sympathy] Bias.)

References/Recommended Readings

Elliott, T. R., & Frank, R. G. (1990). Social and interpersonal reactions to depression and disability. *Rehabilitation Psychology, 35*(3), 135–147.

Elliott, T. R., MacNair, R. R., Yoder, B., & Byrne, C. A. (1991). Interpersonal behavior moderates "kindness norm" effects on cognitive and affective reactions to physical disability. *Rehabilitation Psychology, 36*(1), 57–66.

Fine, M., & Asch, A. (1988). Disability beyond stigma: Social interaction, discrimination, and activism. *Journal of Social Issues, 44,* 3–21.

Kleck, R. E. (1968). Physical stigma and nonverbal cues emitted in face-to-face interaction. *Human Relations, 21,* 19–28.

Wright, B. A. (1988). Attitudes and the fundamental negative bias: Conditions and corrections. In H. Yuker (Ed.), *Attitudes toward persons with disabilities* (pp. 3–21). New York: Springer Publishing Co.

LEARNED HELPLESSNESS. A syndrome of behavioral deficits that result from exposure to noncontingent aversive events. *Usage Notes and Comments:* Learned helplessness is a term coined by Seligman and his co-workers and later expanded in the form of a reformulated model using attribution theory (Peterson & Seligman, 1984). People are said to experience learned helplessness, a phenomenon that is often accompanied by profound depression, when they lose the belief that their own actions can influence the course of their lives (Seligman, 1975). Research indicates that learned helplessness is most likely to occur when people hold themselves personally responsible for their situations, perceive the situations as long-term, or believe that the situations are caused by global rather than specific factors (Garber & Seligman, 1980). However, it should be noted that some behaviors that appear to reflect learned helplessness may actually be adaptive responses to an environment that does not offer alternatives to continued victimization (Flannery & Harvey, 1991).

In rehabilitation, the theory of learned helplessness is based on the phenotypic similarity between disability and illness and the learned-helplessness behavioral syndrome (e.g., lack of response initiation, passivity). Thus, disability is seen as a phenomenon of increased vulnerability and passivity. (*See also:* Attribution; Learned Resourcefulness.)

References

Flannery, R., & Harvey, M. (1991). Psychological trauma and learned helplessness: Seligman's paradigm reconsidered. *Psychotherapy, 28,* 374–378.

Garber, D. S., & Seligman, M. E. P. (1980). *Human helplessness.* New York: Academic Press.

Peterson, C., & Seligman, M. E. P. (1984). Causal explanations as a risk factor for depression; Theory and evidence. *Psychological Review, 91,* 347–374.

Seligman, M. E. P. (1975). *Helplessness: On depression, development and death.* San Francisco: Freeman.

LEARNED RESOURCEFULNESS. A variable that

refers to how well an individual can self-regulate to reduce the disruptive reactions of negative cognitions and the strong affect associated with stressful events. *Usage Notes and Comments:* Critical examination of how the concept of learned resourcefulness may be a predictor of coping with adversity can be found in Rosenbaum (1983) and Clanton, Rude, and Taylor (1992). Rosenbaum (1980) developed the Self-Control Schedule (SCS) to assess an individual's learned resourcefulness. The SCS theoretically evaluates one's ability to implement problem-solving skills, postpone instant gratification, believe that they can self-regulate internal processes, and use cognition to contend with emotional and physiological reaction. Rosenbaum and Palmer (1984) found that highly resourceful study participants with epilepsy coped better with seizures and used more self-control skills than unresourceful participants with epilepsy. Rosenbaum and Smira (1986) found that highly resourceful participants were more effective at delaying gratification if necessary for hemodialysis. (*See also:* Adaptation; Learned Helplessness.)

References

Clanton, L. D., Rude, S. S., & Taylor, C. (1992). Learned resourcefulness as a moderator burnout in a sample of rehabilitation providers. *Rehabilitation Psychology, 37*(2), 131–140.

Rosenbaum, M. (1980). A schedule for assessing self-control behaviors: Preliminary findings. *Behavior Therapy, 11,* 109–121.

Rosenbaum, M. (1983). Learned resourcefulness as a behavioral repertoire for the self-regulation of internal events: Issues and speculations. In M. Rosenbaum, C. M. Franks, & Y. Jaffe (Eds.), *Perspectives on behavior therapy in the epileptic* (pp. 54–70). New York: Springer Publishing Co.

Rosenbaum, M., & Palmon, N. (1984). Helplessness and resourcefulness in coping with epilepsy. *Journal of Consulting and Clinical Psychology, 52,* 244–253.

Rosenbaum, M., & Smira, K. B. (1986). Cognitive and personality factors in the delay of gratification of hemodialysis patients. *Journal of Personality and Social Psychology, 51,* 357–364.

LEAST RESTRICTIVE ENVIRONMENT. A term included in the Education For All Handicapped Children Act of 1975 (PL 94-142), which expresses the importance of using environments for programming and treatment for persons with disabilities that maximize their vocational potential and community integration. *Usage Notes and Comments:* In the early 1970s, a move toward deinstitutionalization occurred, with the goal of reducing the census of state institutions for people with developmental disabilities by one-third; later its meaning widened to denote the process by which persons with disabilities should be treated and served in community environments (Wright, 1980). Since 1971, a number of court cases have supported the principle of a person's legal right to receive treatment and programming in the "least restrictive environment." In essence, the courts declared that a residential facility would be used only as a last resort and only if the individual's needs could be adequately met in that type of setting. The case of Wyatt v. Stickney, 34PSupp 387 (M.D., AL 1972) was precedent-setting in this connection. It declared specifically that the constitutional rights of a person with mental retardation were being violated in an Alabama public school.

The Education for All Handicapped Children Act of 1975 does not define the words "least restrictive environment," but the meaning is implied. To the maximum extent appropriate, children with disabilities in public or private institutions or other care facilities are educated with children who are not labeled as having disabilities, and the use of alternatives such as special classes, separate schooling, or other removal of children with disabilities from the regular educational environment occurs only when the nature or severity of the disability is such that education in regular classes with the use of supplementary aids and services cannot be achieved satisfactorily (20 U.S.C. 1412(5)(B). (*See also:* Americans with Disabilities Act of 1990.)

References/Recommended Readings

Biklen, D. (1982). The least restrictive environment: Its application to education. *Child and Youth Services, 5*(1–2), 121–144.

Dubow, S. (1989). "Into the turbulent mainstream"—A legal perspective on the weight to be given to the least restrictive environment in placement decisions for deaf children. *Journal of Law and Education, 18*(2), 215–228.

Schinnar, A. P., Kamis-Gould, E., Delucia, N., & Rothbard, A. B. (1990). Organizational determinants of efficiency and effectiveness in mental health partial care programs. *Health Services Research, 25*(2), 387–420.

Shallcross, H. M. (1992). Unraveling the mystery of mental health services. *HR Focus, 69*(8), 9.

Stoefen-Fisher, J. M., & Balk, J. (1992). Educational programs for children with hearing loss: Least restrictive environment. *The Volta Review, 94*(1), 19–28.

Wright, G. N. (1980). *Total rehabilitation.* Boston: Little, Brown and Company.

LOSS RESOLUTION. The successful termination of the psychological processes of bereavement (whereby the person experiencing a loss gradually undoes the bond that ties him to the deceased person or other object) and mourning (the psychological process set in motion by the death of a loved object and which, when completed, is associated with the relinquishing of that object). *Usage Notes and Comments:* Usually applied to the death experience, the concept of loss resolution is readily and usefully generalized to the field of disability and rehabilitation. Here, the concept of loss resolution is widened to encompass notions of loss of functioning, physical acumen, loss of a body part, psychological identity (sense of self), and dreams of the future that have been curtailed by the presence of a disability. Nonetheless, the process of loss resolution is conceptualized as being identical to that of the death of a loved one.

The normal process of loss resolution in adults has been observed and changes in emotions, thoughts, and behaviors have been measured over time, as have the emergence of physical symptoms following loss. A predictable cluster of reactions or "phases" that occur in grief and that change over time have been identified, although there is substantial individual variation in terms of the specific manifestations of grief and in the speed with which people move through the process. The usual stages or phases of loss resolution are (1) numbness, shock, and disbelief, (2) protest and anguish, and (3) mourning and restitution. When this process is successfully completed, energy is again available for investment in new relationships and activities, and a bereaved person no longer feels tied to his or her former identity.

Obstacles to loss resolution as described by Worden (1987) include: (1) relational factors, such as losses that are uncertain (e.g., there is hope of regained functioning) and multiple losses; (2) historical factors, such as earlier losses that have not been successfully resolved; (3) personality factors, such as excessive fear of loss of control or dependence; and, (4) social factors such as social isolation and socially unspeakable losses such as disability that occurs during a rape or other socially stigmatized event. (*See also:* Anticipatory Grief; Developmental Stage Model.)

References/Recommended Readings

Bristor, M. (1984). The birth of a handicapped child—a holistic model for grieving. *Family Relations, 33,* 25–32.

Parkes, C. M., & Weiss, R. S. (1983). *Recovery from bereavement.* New York: Basic Books.

Parkes, C. M. (1987-1988). Research: Bereavement. *Omega, 18*(4), 365–377.

Rolland, J. S. (1988). A conceptual model of chronic and life-threatening illness and its impact on families. In C. S. Chilman, E. W. Nunnally, & F. M. Cox, (Eds.), *Chronic illness and disability* (pp. 17–68). Newbury Park, CA: Sage.

Worden, J. W. (1987). *Grief counseling and grief therapy.* New York: Springer Publishing Co.

MAINSTREAMING. The integration of persons with disabilities into society. *Usage Notes and Comments:* This term is primarily used to refer to the integration of children with disabilities into schools and classrooms with nondisabled children. It includes various degrees of integration, ranging from having the child with the disability spending 100% of school time in a class with mostly able-bodied children, to having the child spend a small percentage of the time in such a class. Some children in mainstreamed classes spend part of the day in a resource room where they receive remedial education.

Many studies have been conducted to determine the effects of mainstreaming on both children with and without disabilities. Most reveal that mainstreamed children with disabilities tend to show increased academic achievement, social skills, and self-esteem when compared to those who attend special classes. Although it is occasionally maintained that mainstreaming has negative effects on children without disabilities, this observation has seldom been empirically demonstrated. Instead, several studies have demonstrated that such children show more positive attitudes toward persons with disabilities who have been educated in classes with mainstreamed children. There also is evidence that mainstreaming enhances friendships between children with and without disabilities, although the friendship is often limited to the school situation. Effects of mainstreaming on the attitudes of nondisabled children are often related to the characteristics of the child with the disability and the type of interaction that occurs. For example, tutoring often results in positive attitudes.

References/Recommended Readings

Carlberg, C., & Kavale, K. (1980). The efficacy of special versus regular class placement for exceptional children: A meta-analysis. *Journal of Special Education, 14,* 295–309.

Madden, M. A., & Slavin, R. R. (1983). Mainstreaming students with mild handicaps: Academic and social outcomes. *Review of Educational Research, 53,* 519–569.

Selend, S. J. (1984). Factors contributing to the development of successful mainstreaming programs. *Exceptional Children, 50,* 409–419.

MAJOR LIFE ACTIVITIES. Functional tasks such as caring for oneself, performing manual tasks, walking, seeing, hearing, speaking, breathing, learning, and working. *Usage Notes and Comments:* This term is used in Section 1630.2(i) of

Title I, the Employment Provisions, of the Americans with Disabilities Act of 1990 (ADA) and adapts the definition of the term "major life activities" found in the regulations implementing Section 504 of the Rehabilitation Act of 34CFR Part 104. Major life activities are those basic activities that the average person in the general population can perform with little or no difficulty. The list provided in the interpretive guidance provided by the Equal Opportunity Commission (1991) to assist in understanding of the regulations of the ADA includes other major life activities such as sitting, standing, lifting, and reaching. This listing is meant not to be exhaustive but to illustrate the kinds of activities that are to be considered when formulating a definition of disability in order to determine whether or not a person is a "covered entity" under the Americans with Disabilities Act of 1990. Under the ADA, the definition of the term "disability" is divided into three parts, and an individual must satisfy at least one of these parts in order to be considered an individual with a disability under the Act. In the first part of the definition, an individual is considered to have a "disability" if that person has a physical or mental impairment which substantially limits one or more of that person's major life activities. (*See also:* Americans with Disabilities Act of 1990).

References

Equal Employment Opportunity Commission and U.S. Department of Justice (1991). *Americans with Disabilities Act Handbook*. Washington, DC: Author.

MEDICAL MODEL. A disease-oriented approach to the identification and treatment of physical and/or behavioral dysfunction. *Usage Notes and Comments:* Considered the major orientation used by many physicians, the emphasis of the medical model is on the diagnosis and labeling of an individual's disabling condition based on identifiable features of specific diseases or disorders. Compared to other models of human behavior (e.g., learning theory, ecological approach), the model may ignore or assign less importance to psychological and socioenvironmental factors that may be contributing to the diagnosed condition and/or affecting response to treatment. Under the medical model, the professional is usually active while the patient is passive. To many, a scene in the typical physician's office is one in which the patient is lying horizontally and passively while the professional actively does something to him, either in examining or treatment. This model is contrasted to that typically used by many trained in the behavioral and social sciences whereby the helping professional assists the client in gaining insight and planning future actions. (*See Also:* B=F[P,O,E].)

References/Recommended Readings

Barker, R. L. (1987). *The social work dictionary*. Silver Spring, MD: National Association of Social Workers.

Campbell, R. J. (1989). *Psychiatry dictionary* (6th ed.). New York: Oxford University Press.

Zastrow, C., & Kirst-Ashman, K. (1990). *Understanding human behavior and the social environment* (2nd ed.). Chicago: Nelson-Hall.

MOURNING, REQUIREMENT OF.

A psychological construct which, when used in the field of rehabilitation, describes the expectation or demand made on persons with disability to mourn their disability and situation. *Usage Notes and Comments:* The requirement of mourning concept, developed by Baker, Wright, and Gonick (1946) and Wright (1955), considers the expectation to be depressed over loss and to brood or mourn to be almost universally imposed on persons with disabilities. On the part of persons with disabilities, mourning has frequently been observed, especially soon after the onset of disablement, along with such related affective responses as self-devaluation and the generalization of dysfunctional anxiety (Wright, 1960). Significant others, that is, those persons who are closest to and psychologically important to individuals with disabilities, also experience the "mourning" response in what can be viewed as a sympathetic response because of overidentification with the person with the disability. However, above and beyond such natural responses to loss from disability, nondisabled persons who are not significant others may require the individual with a disability to mourn. Possible reasons for this may be that they are personally threatened by the person's medical condition or have a need to feel psychologically superior. (*See also:* Expectation Discrepancy; Interpersonal Theory; Somatopsychology.)

References

Baker, R., Wright, B., & Gonick, M. (1946). *Adjustment to physical handicap and illness: A survey of the social psychology of physique and disability.* New York: Social Sciences Research Council.

Wright, B. A. (1955). The period of mourning in chronic illness. In R. Harrower (Ed.), *Medical and psychological teamwork in the care of the chronically ill.* Springfield, IL: Charles C Thomas.

Wright, B. A. (1983). *Physical disability—A psychosocial approach* (2nd ed.). New York: Harper & Row.

NEGOTIATED-OUTCOMES MODEL. The presentation of certain aspects of self for which persons would like to be known by others. *Usage Notes and Comments:* This model regards persons with physical disabilities as active participants in the labeling process by considering the manner in which they present themselves to others. For example, the negotiated-outcomes model, as applied to appearance, posits that persons with physical disabilities regard dress and personal adornment as presenting certain aspects of self for which they would like to be known to other persons. This model considers the manner in which persons with disabilities present themselves so as to receive positive social feedback (Hanks & Poplin, 1981). (*See also:* Compensatory Model; Prejudice by Invitation.)

References/Recommended Readings

Hanks, M., & Poplin, D. E. (1981). The sociology of physical disability. A review of the literature and some conceptual perspectives. *Deviant Behavior, 2,* 309–328.

Kaiser, S. B., Wingate, S. B., Freeman, C. M., & Chandler, J. L.

(1987). Acceptance of physical disability and attitudes toward personal appearance. *Rehabilitation Psychology, 32*(1), 51–58.

Levitin, T. E. (1975). Deviants as active participants in the labeling process: The visibly handicapped. *Social Problems, 22*, 548–557.

NEUROMUSCULAR REEDUCATION.

Therapeutic exercise designed to facilitate recovery of various degrees of voluntary control of paralyzed muscles through techniques emphasizing biofeedback to guide the performance of the person with the disability. *Usage Notes and Comments:* The term "neuromuscular reeducation" was coined to describe therapeutic procedures that enabled persons with poliomyelitis to regain control of muscles that were temporarily weakened or paralyzed. More recently, the term has been used with regard to treatment of persons with peripheral or central neuropathies and reconstructive articular surgery. The therapist may provide feedback verbally, or by means of apparatus such as electromyography, of which the latter provides an auditory or visual signal to the person.

References/Recommended Readings

Middaugh, S. J. (1978). EMG feedback as a muscle re-education technique: A controlled study. *Physical Therapy, 58*, 11–15.

Mroczek, N., Halpern, D., McHugh, R. (1978). Electromyographic feedback and physical therapy for neuromuscular retraining in hemiplegia. *Archives of Physical Medicine and Rehabilitation, 59*, 258–262.

NONHANDICAPPING LANGUAGE.

Language that maintains the integrity of individuals as whole human beings by avoiding expressions that (a) imply that the person as a whole is disabled (e.g., "disabled person"), (b) equate people with their condition (e.g., "epileptics"), (c) have superfluous, negative overtones (e.g., "polio victim"), (d) are regarded as a slur (e.g., "cripple"), and (e) metaphorically extend negative connotations of an impairment (e.g., "blind to the conditions").

Usage Notes and Comments: The use of certain words or phrases can express gender, ethnic, or racial bias, either intentionally or unintentionally. The same is true of language referring to persons with disabilities, which in many instances expresses negative and disparaging attitudes.

It is recommended that the word "disability" be used to refer to an attribute of a person, and "handicap" to the *source* of limitations. Sometimes a disability itself may handicap a person, as when a person with one arm is handicapped in playing the violin. However, when the limitation is environmental, as in the case of attitudinal, legal, and architectural barriers, the disability is *not* handicapping—the environmental factor is. This distinction is important because the environment is frequently overlooked as a major source of limitation, even when it is far more limiting than the disability. Thus, prejudice handicaps people by denying access to opportunities: inaccessible buildings handicap people who require the use of a ramp.

Use of the terms "nondisabled" or "persons without disabilities" is preferable to the term "normal" when comparing persons with disabilities to others. Usage of "normal" makes the unconscious comparison of abnormal, thus stigmatizing those individuals with differences. For example, state "a nondisabled control group," not "a normal control group."

For decades, persons with disabilities have been identified first by their disability and second as a person. Often, persons with disabilities are viewed as being afflicted with, or being a victim of, a disability. In focusing on the disability, an individual's strengths, abilities, skills, and resources are often ignored. In many instances, persons with disabilities are viewed as not having the capacity or right to express their goals and preferences, nor are persons with disabilities seen as resourceful and contributing members of society. Many words and phrases commonly used when discussing persons with disabilities reflect these biases.

Listed below are examples of negative, stereotypical, and sometimes offensive words and expressions used when referring to or discussing persons with disabilities. Also listed are examples of preferred language that describes without implying a negative judgement. Even though their connotations may change with time, the rationale behind the use of these expresions provides a basis for language re-evaluation. The specific recommendations are not intended to be all inclusive. The basic principles, however, apply in the formulation of all nonhandicapping language.

EXPRESSIONS TO BE AVOIDED	PREFERRED EXPRESSIONS
1. Put people first, not their disability	
disabled person	person with (who has) a disability
defective child	child with a congenital disability; child with a birth impairment
mentally ill person	person with mental illness or psychiatric disability

Preferred expressions avoid the implication that the person as a whole is disabled or defective.

2. Do not label people by their disability	
epileptics	individuals with epilepsy
amputee	person with an amputation
paraplegics	individuals with paraplegia
schizophrenics	people who have schizophrenia
the disabled	people with disabilities
the retarded	children with mental retardation
the mentally ill	people with a mental illness or psychiatric disability
the CMI or SPMI	people with long term or serious and persistent mental illness or psychiatric disabilities

Because the person is *not* the disability, the two concepts should be separate.

3. Do not label persons with disabilities as patients or invalids

These names imply that a person is sick or under a doctor's care. People with disabilities should not be referred to as patients or invalids unless their illness status (if any) is under discussion or unless they are currently residing in a hospital.

4. *Do not overextend the severity of a disability*

the physically disabled	individuals with a physical disability
the learning disabled	children with specific learning disabilities
retarded adult	adult with *mental* retardation
chronic mental illness	long-term or persistent mental illness or psychiatric disability

Preferred expressions limit the scope of the disability. Even if a person has a particular physical disability, this does not mean that the person is unable to do all physical activities. Similarly, a child with a learning disability does not have difficulty in all areas of learning, nor does *mental* retardation imply retardation in all aspects of development. Chronicity in physical illness often implies a permanent situation, but persons with psychiatric disabilities are able to recover.

5. *Use emotionally neutral expression*

stroke victim	individual who had a stroke
afflicted with cerebral palsy	person with cerebral palsy
suffering from multiple sclerosis	people who have multiple sclerosis

Objectionable expressions have excessive, negative overtones and suggest continued helplessness.

6. *Emphasize abilities, not limitations*

confined to a wheelchair	uses a wheelchair
homebound	child who is taught at home
The person is not confined to a wheelchair but uses it for mobility, nor is a person homebound who is taught or works at home.	

7. *Avoid the offensive expressions*

cripple	person who has a limp
deformed	person with a shortened arm

| mongoloid | child with Down Syndrome |
| crazy, paranoid | person with symptoms of mental illness |

8. Focus on the right and capacity of people with disabilities to express their own goals and preferences, and to exercise control over their own services and supports

placement	discussion of suitable and preferred living arrangements
professional judgement	include a consideration of a person's goals and preferences
patient management, case management	care coordination, supportive services, resource coordination, assistance

In many instances, persons with disabilities are not given opportunities to participate in decisions regarding the services or supports they will receive as part of a treatment or rehabilitation program. Instead, they are viewed as requiring "management" as patients or "cases" rather than as individuals with goals and preferences that should be taken into account.

9. Seeing people with disabilities as a resource and as contributing community members, not as a burden or problem

family burden	family supports needs
problem or mental illness or of the mentally ill	challenges which people with psychiatric disabilities face
community supports need of individuals	responsibility of communities for inclusion and support

Discussions regarding the service needs of persons with disabilities and their families often use terms that define the individual as a burden or a problem. Instead, terms which reflect the special needs of these persons are preferable, with a clear recognition of the responsibility of communities for inclusion and support of persons with disabilities.

(American Psychological Association, Committee on Disability Issues in Psychology (1992). *Guidelines for non-handicapping language in ADA journals.* Copyright © 1992 by the American Psychological Association. Reprinted by permission.)

References/Recommended Readings

Wright, B. A. (1983). *Physical disability—a psychosocial approach* (2nd ed.). Chapter 1. New York: Harper-Collins.

NORMALIZATION. See Accommodation; Devaluation, Normalization Principle.

NORMALIZATION PRINCIPLE. The use of culturally valued means in order to enable, establish, and/or maintain valued social roles. *Usage Notes and Comments:* A concept originated by the Swedish proponent Nirje (1969), this principle affirms that the conditions of everyday life for people with disabilities should approximate the norms and patterns of the mainstream of society as closely as possible. Wolfensberger (1980) suggests that the principle of normalization can be conceptualized as having seven core themes.

1. The role of (un)consciousness in health involves the identification of unconscious, and usually negative, dynamics within human services that contribute to the devaluation and oppression of certain groups of people in a society. Conscious strategies can be provided to remediate the devalued social status of such people.
2. Role expectancy and role circularity are important factors in deviancy making and deviancy unmasking.
3. The Conservatism Corollary: The more vulnerable a person is to societal devaluation, the greater is the impact reduction/prevention of any such vulnerabilities and/or the balancing off of such vulnerabilities by positively valued manifestations or compensations.
4. The Developmental Model and Personal-Competency Enhancement: Enhancement of personal competencies of members of society who are devalued.
5. The Power of Imitation: Capitalizing on the dynamic of imitation in a positive way so that the role models provided to persons who are devalued are people who function routinely in an appropriate and valued fashion.
6. The Dynamics and Relevance of Social Imagery: Incorpora-

tion of positive imagery in messages about individuals who are devalued.

7. The Importance of Societal Integration and Valued Social Participation: The tendency to reject and segregate persons who are socially devalued.(See also: Accommodation; Devaluation; Spread; Stigma.)

References/Recommended Readings

Nirje, B (1969). The normalization principle and its human management. In R. B. Kugeland & W. Wolfensberger (Eds.), *Changing patterns in residential services for the mentally retarded.* Washington, DC: U.S. Government Printing Office.

Wolfensberger, W. (1980). The definition of normalization: Update, problems, disagreements, and misunderstandings. In R. J. Flynn & K. E. Nitsch (Eds.), *Normalization, social integration, and community services.* Baltimore: University Park Press.

Wolfensberger, W., & Tullman, S. (1982). A brief outline of the principle of normalization. *Rehabilitation Psychology, 27(3),* 131–146.

OVERLAPPING SITUATIONS. Two or more different psychological situations that may exert conflicting role expectations or determinants of behavior on a person with a disability, which may result in such affective reactions as uncertainty, anxiety, frustration, and erratic or disrupted behavior. *Usage Notes and Comments:* A concept developed in somatopsychology (see Barker, Wright, Myerson, & Gonick, 1953; Wright, 1983) to explain unusual or erratic behavior on the part of persons with disabilities. As stated by Wright (1983):

Persons with a disability, like numbers of other minority groups, may be represented as subject to two different and often conflicting situations at the same time. On the one hand, considered disabled, they are subject to the expectations of how a person with a disability should act (disabled determinants of behavior); on the other hand, the wish to be "just like everyone else" predisposes them toward "normal" patterns of behavior. (p. 19)

The concept of overlapping situations may also be used in explaining behavior in relation to characteristics of people other than individuals with disabilities, including minority group status. For example, both Barker et al. (1953) and Wright (1983) discuss overlapping situations in understanding the affective reactions and erratic behavior of adolescents, viewing them as being influenced by the conflicting role and behavior expectations of the two overlapping psychological situations of adulthood and childhood. Another example of overlapping situations might be provided by a woman functioning as a top business executive, where traditional feminine role and behavior expectations may often be in conflict with behavior and role expectations of a business executive. (*See also:* Interpersonal Theory; Somatopsychology.)

References

Barker, R. G., Wright, B. A., Myerson, L., & Gonick, M. R. (1953). *Adjustment to physical handicap and illness: A survey of the social psychology of physique and disability* (2nd ed.). New York: Social Science Research Council, Bulletin 55.
Wright, B. A. (1983). *Physical disability—A psychosocial approach.* New York: Harper & Row.

PERSON–ENVIRONMENT (P x E) MODEL.   See Trait-and-Factor Approach.

PLISSIT MODEL.   A conceptual scheme frequently employed in sex counseling and therapy for persons with disabilities. *Usage Notes and Comments:* Developed by Anon (1976), the PLISSIT model provides a format for dealing with sexual dysfunction structured into four stages. The first level of therapy is *permission (P)*. In this stage, permission for resumption of sexual activity is given.

In the second stage, *limited information (LI),* a discussion of the physical impact of therapy and the alterations that can be expected in sexual function is offered. The brief and simple discussion serves to inform the couple that sexual gratification is still possible in spite of, for example, absence of penile erection or ejaculation. Information provided is directly relevant to the individual's specific problems.

The third stage, *specific suggestions (SS),* is problem-oriented. The therapist provides instructions regarding techniques of sexual foreplay and mutual pleasuring, the use of marital aides, and alternatives to vaginal intercourse.

The fourth level is *intensive therapy (IT).* Because erectile impotence is the most common form of sexual dysfunction, this level can include surgical implantation of a penile prosthesis.

References/Recommended Readings

Anon, J. S. (1976). *The behavioral treatment of sexual problems: Brief therapy.* New York: Harper & Row.

Cole, T. M., & Cole, S. S. (1990). Rehabilitation of problems of sexuality in physical disability. In E. H. Wickland, Jr. (Ed.), *Krugen's handbook of physical medicine and rehabilitation* (4th ed.). Philadelphia: W. B. Saunders.

POSITIVITY (SYMPATHY) BIAS. The tendency of individuals to evaluate persons with disabilities with more lenient criteria than that typically extended to others, and to subsequently behave in a manner that appears to convey positive, accepting, and favorable opinions of persons with disabilities. *Usage Notes and Comments:* It is believed that the roots of the positivity bias lie in ambivalent attitudes toward persons with disability; that is, a person may feel sympathy and aversion simultaneously toward a person who is stigmatized. In order to reduce the tension created by the presence of the disability, an individual may choose to honor a social norm to treat a person with a disability kindly. This behavior may be reflected in obsequious offers of help, inflated opinions of performance, or in stated opinions that approximate the expressed opinions of the person with a disability that are at variance to the prior stated opinions of the study participants.

Expressions of the positivity bias may be particularly sensitive to perceived social norms of desired behavior. Individuals often avoid or cease interaction with a person with a disability once a convenient and socially acceptable option is provided. When the behavior of the person with a disability becomes more personally relevant to a nondisabled individual, these attitudes may become polarized and response amplification may occur.

Several alternative views and criticisms of this construct should be noted. Much of the well-controlled research on the positivity bias has relied on contrived laboratory experiments involving strangers (usually college students) in which the disability of one was made artificially salient. These experiments establish a context that disregards the real-life interpersonal strategies often employed by persons with disability. Furthermore, it is possible that overt positive responses of study participants to a person with a disability may reflect genuine surprise in reaction to nonstereotypic behavior of the target. (*See also:* Kindness Norm; Stigma; Sympathy Bias.)

References/Recommended Readings

Gibbons, F. X., Stephan, W. G., Stephenson, B., & Petty, C. R. (1980). Reactions to stigmatized others: Response amplification vs. sympathy. *Journal of Experimental Social Psychology, 16,* 591–605.

Katz, I. (1981). *Stigma: A social psychological analysis.* Hillsdale, NJ: Lawrence Erlbaum.

Kleck, R. E. (1968). Physical stigma and nonverbal cues emitted in face to face interactions. *Human Relations, 21,* 19–28.

Snyder, M. L., Kleck, R. E., Strenta, A., & Mentzer, S. (1979). Avoidance of the handicapped: An attributional ambiguity analysis. *Journal of Personality and Social Psychology, 37,* 2297–2306.

Wright, B. A. (1988). Attitudes and the fundamental negative bias: Conditions and corrections. In H. Yuker (Ed.), *Attitudes toward persons with disability* (pp. 3–21). New York: Springer Publishing Co.

PREJUDICE BY INVITATION. A role-theory concept which hypothesizes that much of the negative interaction occurring between persons with and without disabilities is the result of uncertainty about appropriate role expectations and role enactments. (*See also:* Social Role Theory.)

Recommended Reading

English, R. W. (1977). The application of personality theory to explain psychological reactions to physical disability (pp. 90–129). In R. P. Marinelli & A. E. Dell Orto (Eds.), *The psychological and social impact of physical disability*. New York: Springer Publishing Co.

PSYCHOGOGY. Psychosocial intervention strategies based on an educational model. *Usage Notes and Comments:* The word psychogogy was coined by Maslow (1963) to denote educational treatment approaches, which are distinct from therapeutic or curative strategies. Vash (1981) adopted the term to designate psychosocial-vocational (PSV) service techniques in rehabilitation that emphasize prevention through strengthening of client capabilities. According to Vash, the salient features of psychogogic interventions are: educational model, prevention, teaching, strengthening, informing and guiding strong Eastern influence, holistic living, client responsibility, and promoting psychological well-being. Specific techniques that Vash discusses under the psychogogic category include traditional approaches such as career counseling, personal counseling, social casework, and teaching techniques that incorporate an Eastern influence, including the martial arts, yoga, and meditation.

References

Maslow, A. (1963). *Eupsychian management*. Homewood, IL: Richard Irwin.
Vash, C. L. (1981). *The psychology of disability*. New York: Springer Publishing Co.

QUALIFIED HANDICAPPED PERSON. A legal term that defines whether an impairment affects one's ability to perform a job for which the individual is otherwise eligible in possessing the education and experience. *Usage Notes and Comments:* In E. E. Black v. Marshall, a federal court directed that the definition of "qualified handicapped person" be determined on a case-by-case basis, stating that

The definitions contained in the [Rehabilitation] Act are personal and must be evaluated by looking at the particular individual. A handicapped individual is one who has a physical or mental disability which for such an individual constitutes or results in a substantial handicap to employment . . . It is the impaired individual that must be examined and not just the impairment in the abstract. . . . A person who has obtained a graduate degree in chemistry and is then turned down for a chemist's job because of an impairment is not likely to be heartened by the news that he can still be a streetcar conductor, an attorney or a forest ranger. (Emer & Frink, 1983, p. 646)

The Black decision demonstrates the gap between the legal model of discrimination and the situation of workers with handicaps. Before a court can analyze whether an employer's behavior is discriminatory, it must first engage in a complex and lengthy evaluation of whether the plaintiff is a member of the minority that the law intends to protect. Recent court decisions on conditions that may or may not be regarded as handicaps include: AIDS (contagious diseases are a handicap, but whether persons with such diseases can be reasonably accommodated must be decided on a case-by-case basis); marijuana use (not a handicap); varicose veins (not a handicap, if the condition was mild to moderate); diabetes (a handicap); and, crossed eyes (not a handicap). (*See also:* Americans with Disabilities Act of 1990; Disability; Handicap; Impairment; Reasonable Accommodation; Vocational Rehabilitation Act (VRA) of 1973.)

References/Recommended Readings

Berkowitz, M., & Hill, M. A. (Eds.) (1986). *Disability and the labor market.* Ithaca, NY: ILR Press—Cornell University.
Emer, W. H., & Frink, C. B. (1983). E E Black and beyond: Update on hiring the handicapped. *Labor Law Journal, 34,* 643–653.

QUALITY-OF-LIFE.   Aspects of daily life that collectively are construed as positive and render a feeling that life is worth living. *Usage Notes and Comments:* This term has been defined in a variety of ways including a person's ability to perform ordinary activities of daily life (Alexander & Willems, 1981) and the ability to realize life plans (Cohen, 1982). In addition to differences in definition, a wide variety of specific areas of life have been examined in quality-of-life studies.

Quality-of-life assessment has evolved from a number of diverse fields, notably the social sciences and public administration. Although originally focused on objective, gross indicators of well-being such as economic indicators, a subjective domain, which includes perceived needs and satisfaction with living conditions has increasingly been recognized. This subjective domain derives from a judgment of our life used as a comparison of our life condition relative to those of others. Although these two domains are interrelated, the latter seems more closely linked to individual actions or behaviors, and therefore may be especially useful in understanding response to treatment.

Although health has been one of the most prominent and universally accepted quality-of-life constituents, development of qualitative indicators in this area has lagged. Often, consideration has been limited to factors such as the presence or absence of disease, life expectancies, and morbidity rates, without concern for the impact of illness or disability on daily life. However, recent advances in medical technology (e.g., dialysis and artificial heart implants) have resulted in increased concern with quality-of-life issues within the health care community.

Interest in quality-of-life assessment has emerged in the field of rehabilitation. There has been a call for expanding traditional indices of the impact of rehabilitation interventions and programming beyond changes in functional level or financial benefits associated with a return to the work force (Cardus, Fuhrer, & Thrall, 1981; Alexander and Williams, 1981). This need for expanding rehabilitation indicators stems from recognition that many nonmonetary, nonobjective benefits accrue from rehabilitation, such as enhanced personal dignity and self-esteem (Kottke, 1982). Consequently, there is a need to assess the impact of rehabilitation services in a more comprehensive manner.

Other efforts involving life-quality measurement concepts in health care include that of Blau (1977), who demonstrated use of quality-of-life indicators as the basis for evaluating treatment impact on persons with psychiatric disabilities, and Padilla, Presant, and Grant (1983), who developed a disease-specific instrument for use with individuals with cancer. Some health care researchers (for example, Baird, Adams, & Aosman, 1985) have approached quality-of-life assessment by surveying functional limitations, using instruments such as the Level of Rehabilitation Scale (Carey & Posavac, 1978) and the Sickness Impact Profile (Bergner, Bobbitt, & Pollard, 1976).

Although these studies support the utility of quality-of-life assessment in research on some health-care issues, the instruments are limited in the range of application, either because they are disease specific or because they are concerned only with objective indicators (i.e., functional deficits). Consequently, the meaning of the functional deficits to the persons who manifest them must be based on assumption or imagination, which is risky without verification and a means by which to establish relevance to the total life situation. (*See also:* Adaptation.)

References/Recommended Readings

Alexander, J., & Williams, E. P. (1981). Quality of life: Some measurement requirements. *Archives of Physical Medicine and Rehabilitation, 62,* 261–265.

Baird, A. D., Adams, K. M., & Aosman, J. I. (1985). Medical neuropsychological and quality of life correlates of cerebrovascular disease. *Rehabilitation Psychology, 30,* 145–155.

Bergner, M., Bobbitt, R. A., & Pollard, W. F. (1976). The sickness impact profile validation of a health status measure. *Medical Care, 14,* 57–67.

Blau, T. H. (1977). Quality of life, social indicators, and predictors of change. *Professional Psychology, 8,* 464–473.

Cardus, D. R., Fuhrer, J. J., & Thrall, R. M. (1981). Quality of life in cost-benefit analysis rehabilitation research. *Archives of Physical Medicine and Rehabilitation, 62,* 209–211.

Carey, R. G., & Posavac, E. J. (1978). Program evaluation of a physical medicine and rehabilitation unit: A new approach. *Archives of Physical Medicine and Rehabilitation, 59,* 330–336.

Cohen, C. (1982). On the quality of life: Some philosophical reflections. *Circulation, 66,* 29–33.

Freed, M. M. (1984). Quality of life: The physician's dilemma. *Archives of Physical Medicine and Rehabilitation, 65,* 109–111.

Kottke, K. J. (1982). Philosophic considerations of quality of life for the disabled. *Archives of Physical Medicine and Rehabilitation, 63,* 60–62.

Padilla, Q. V., Presant, C., & Grant, M. (1983). Quality of life index for patients with cancer. *Research Nursing in Health, 6,* 117–126.

Zautra, A., & Goodhart, M. (1979). Quality of life indicators: A review of the literature. *Community Mental Health Review, 40,* 1–10.

REACTANCE. A motivational state aroused when an individual perceives that a specific behavioral freedom (or choice) is threatened with elimination or is eliminated (Breham, 1966). *Usage Notes and Comments:* The importance of personal freedom, the magnitude of the threat of loss of freedom, the authority of the person making the threat, and the expectation of future interactions with that person all affect the degree of reactance arousal (Prandoni & Wall, 1990). When clients with disabilities perceive that their freedom is threatened in assessment or treatment situations, they may seek to restore a sense of freedom and choice (Wright, 1983). For example, when a person with persistent symptoms of an illness is confined to bed rest, he/she may perceive this "order" as a threat to personal freedom. To restore a sense of freedom, the person may respond to the perceived threat with noncompliant behaviors that may be viewed as being uncooperative with the staff. Reactance theorists stress the importance of involving clients in decision making, goal setting, and educational interventions.

References

Breham, J. W. (1966). *A theory of psychological reactance.* New York: Academic Press.

Prandoni, J. R., & Wall, S. M. (1990). Effects of mental health and reactance-reducing information on offenders' compliance with court-mandated psychiatric evaluations. *Professional Psychology: Research and Practice, 21,* 204–209.

Wright, B. A. (1983). *Physical disability—A psychosocial approach* (2nd ed.) (pp. 452). New York: Harper & Row.

REASONABLE ACCOMMODATION. A term in federal law and policy describing requirements for accommodating employees with disabilities. *Usage Notes and Comments:* The "reasonable accommodation" of persons with disabilities by industry has now been part of federal law and policy for a decade. Although the provisions of the Rehabilitation Act of 1973 (P.L. 93-112) and The Americans with Disabilities Act of 1990 enjoyed bipartisan support in Congress, the requirements of reasonable accommodation have been among the more controversial aspects of the implementation of those laws. According to a recent review of federal law relating to accommodation (Berkowitz & Hill, 1986), almost 30 different federal laws prohibit discrimination against individuals with handicaps. Most of the laws originated in the early 1970s when persons with disabilities, along with other groups in American society as part of the larger civil rights movement, sought protections. The Rehabilitation Act of 1973, as amended in 1978, is the principal basis for the reasonable accommodation requirements for private employers. This statute combined the comprehensive federal–state program providing people with handicaps with a wide variety of rehabilitation services, along with broadly worded civil rights protections against discrimination. The law sought to increase their employment skills and the ability to live independently in the community. Title V of the Act established as national policy the protection of the civil rights of individuals with handicaps. The provisions of Title V, and the regulations subsequently issued that interpret the provisions, have been the most controversial elements of the overall legislation. Three key sections of the title have directly affected employers: Sections 504, 501, and 503, with the latter affecting private-sector firms. Section 504 prohibits discrimination on the basis of handicap in any program or activity receiving federal financial assistance. Section 501 focuses on the federal government's own responsibility to be an equal opportunity employer for people with handicaps. Section 503 requires businesses with federal contracts of $2,500 or more to take affirmative action to employ and advance qualified persons with disabilities.

What constitutes "reasonable accommodation" is not defined by the regulations, but Appendix B to the regulations provides a sample notice to employees that describes such accommodations as "the accommodations which we could make which would enable you to perform the job properly and safely, including special equipment, changes in the physical layout of the job, elimination of certain duties relating to the job, or other accommodations" (Collignon, 1986, p. 197). Until passage of the Americans with Disabilities Act of 1990, contractors could plead "business necessity" and costs as grounds for limiting their responsibilities in mitigating the effects of an individual's handicapping condition on job performance. Contractors, under the section, were obligated to undertake a self-analysis of their personnel procedures to ensure that applicants who have a handicap and employees are systematically and thoroughly considered for hiring and promotions. Job qualifications had to be modified to ensure that they were job-related and consistent with business necessity. Depending on the outcome of the self-analysis, employers were advised to publicize their affirmative action policies for recruiting more applicants who have a handicap and for hiring and promoting employees with handicaps. (*See also:* Americans with Disabilities Act of 1990; Disability; Handicap; Qualified Handicapped Person; Vocational Rehabilitation Act of 1973.)

References

Collignon, F. C. (1986). The role of reasonable accommodation in employing disabled persons in private industry. In M. Berkowitz & M. A. Hill. (Eds.) (1986). *Disability and the labor market: Economic problems, policies, and programs.* (pp. 196–241). Ithaca, NY: ILR Press—Cornell University.

REHABILITATION ACT OF 1973. See Vocational Rehabilitation Act of 1973; Americans with Disabilities Act of 1990; Reasonable Accommodation.

Recommended Readings

Baxley, J. F. (1989). Rehabilitating AIDS-based employment discrimination: HIV infection as a handicap under the Voca-

tional Rehabilitation Act of 1973. *Seton Hall Law Review,*
Winter, 23–54.

Harris, G. (1980). Legislation: Rights of the handicapped in
professional training programs under (section) 504 of the
Vocational Rehabilitation Act. *Oklahoma Law Review,*
Spring, 409–429.

Leap, T., & Kovarsky, I. (1980). The age discrimination in
employment and the Vocational Rehabilitation Act: A proposed consolidation. *Labor Law Journal,* January, 13–26.

RESPITE CARE. The provision of care to persons requiring such assistance and living in the community in order to relieve
their regular caregivers. *Usage Notes and Comments:* Demands of
daily and in some cases round-the-clock care for one or more
dependent persons may cause social, psychological, physical, and/
or economic stress to the health care provider. The goal of respite
care is to temporarily reduce the burdens of caregiving.

Respite care can be offered in a range of settings and may vary
in duration. For example, at one end of the continuum, in-home
care can be provided for several hours on a daily or intermittent
basis. At the other end of the continuum, hospitals may have
respite beds where a person can stay for several days or longer,
enabling caregivers to leave town for a vacation. (*See also:*
Burnout).

Recommended Readings

Maddox, G. L. (Ed.). (1987). *The encyclopedia of aging.* New
York: Springer Publishing Co.

Gibson, M. J. S., & Nusberg, C. (1985). *International glossary
of social gerontology.* New York: Van Nostrand Reinhold.

SECONDARY GAIN. Indirect physical or psychological
benefits derived from a disability or illness (Thompson & Byyny,
1989). *Usage Notes and Comments:* Wright (1983) states that
secondary gains may serve to reinforce or maintain "sick role"
behaviors in persons with disabilities.

Although secondary gains typically connote negative behavior, it is important to note that secondary gains can be either
positive or negative depending on the context (Wright, 1983).

An "unhealthy" secondary gain may include an overreliance on others to perform tasks ostensibly associated with the disability or frequently seeking out attention and sympathy. A "healthy" secondary gain may involve viewing oneself as a survivor of a severe medical condition, meeting further difficulties with will, ambition, and effort. (*See also:* Disability; Self-concept; Self-esteem.)

References/Recommended Readings

Marciani, R. D. (1990). Chronic pain: Economic, ethical, and psychosocial considerations. In T. W. Miller, (Ed.), *Chronic pain* (Vols. 1 & 2) (pp. 81–115). Madison, CT: International Universities Press.

Thompson, T. L., & Byyny, R. L. (1989). Pain problems in primary care medical practice. In C. D. Tollison, (Ed.), *Handbook of chronic pain management* (pp. 532–549). Baltimore: Williams & Wilkins.

Thompson, T. L., & Steele, B. F. (1981). The psychological aspects of pain. In R. C. Simions, (Ed.), *Understanding human behavior in health and illness* (pp. 57–63). Baltimore: Williams & Wilkins.

Wright, B. A. (1983). *Physical disability—A psychosocial approach* (2nd ed.). Philadelphia: Harper & Row.

SELF-CONCEPT. Perception of the self as an object based on reflections of one's attitudes, beliefs, values, body image, and experiences. *Usage Notes and Comments:* The development of self-concept is considered to be primarily a cognitive process. This process can be contrasted with a largely affective process of developing self-esteem (the value or worth placed on components of self-concept). The relationship between self-concept and identity has been extensively explored (e.g., the self-concept as an organization of identities). (*See also:* Body Image Theory; Secondary Gain; Self-esteem.)

Recommended Readings

Kuper, A., & Kuper, J. (1985). *The social science encyclopedia.* London: Routledge and Kegan Paul.

Maddox, G. L. (Ed.) (1987). *The encyclopedia of aging.* New York: Springer Publishing Co.

SELF-EFFICACY THEORY. A theoretical explanation of behavior that focuses on the impact of an individual's
expectations of effectiveness. *Usage Notes and Comments:*
According to Bandura (1977), if individuals expect failure, then
it is more likely that they will perform at a sub-standard level
on a particular task; in contrast, if individuals believe that they
will succeed, it may be more likely that the task will be achieved
successfully (Bandura, 1983; Bandura & Cervone, 1983). Efficacy expectations can affect the activities people choose, how hard
they strive, how long they persist, and the successfulness of
their endeavors (Bandura, 1986).

Efficacy expectations arise from four main sources of information: (1) performance accomplishments—the most influential
information, based on personal mastery experiences; (2) vicari-
ous experiences—observing others cope and succeed, or fail and
become frustrated; (3) verbal persuasion, exhortation, and other
types of social influence; and, (4) states of physiological and
emotional arousal from which people judge their level of anxiety
and vulnerability to stress. In addition, cognitive appraisals of
task difficulty will influence the impact of performance accomplishments on perceived self-efficacy. For example, to succeed at
an easy task gives no new information to the person; however,
mastering a hard task provides salient evidence of high competence and skill.

Bandura proposes that psychotherapeutic interventions, such
as behavior therapy, individual psychotherapy, and education
serve as ways of creating and strengthening expectations of
personal effectiveness. Self-efficacy theory is especially important in working with people with disabilities who often are
challenged by beliefs that they cannot maintain important life
roles (e.g., career, marriage) or that they should not waste time
or effort trying different approaches. People with disabilities, as
well as those around them, can alter expectations of personal
efficacy resulting in improved behavioral performance, coping,
and sense of accomplishment.

References/Recommended Readings

Bandura, A. (1977). Self-efficacy: Toward a unifying theory of
behavioral change. *Psychological Review, 84,* 191–215.

Bandura, A. (1983). Self-efficacy determinants of anticipated fears and calamities. *Journal of Personality and Social Psychology, 45,* 464–469.

Bandura, A. (1986). *Social foundations of thought and action: A social cognitive theory.* Englewood Cliffs, NJ: Prentice Hall.

Bandura, A., & Cervone, D. (1983). Self-evaluative and self-efficacy mechanisms governing the motivational effects of goal systems. *Journal of Personality and Social Psychology, 45,* 1017–1028.

Rosenthal, T., & Bandura, A. (1978). Psychological modeling: Theory and practice. In S. Garfield & A. Bergin (Eds.), *Handbook of psychotherapy and behavior change* (pp. 621–658). New York: John Wiley and Sons.

SELF-ESTEEM. A judgment of one's own value or worth. *Usage Notes and Comments:* Primarily affective in nature, self-esteem is an appraisal of the self based on a comparison between expectations and achievements, as well as more socially derived factors such as approval, support, and love. Self-esteem is widely considered to be an important factor affecting mental health, interpersonal relations, competence in activities such as work/leisure, as well as general outlook on life (e.g., optimism or pessimism).

A large body of research has focused on the magnitude and direction of the relationship between self-esteem and self-concept. Low self-esteem is thought to be associated with a poor self-concept, and the inverse has also been postulated. The study of self-esteem enhancement and reduction when a person is facing serious life concerns has shown several social and psychological processes that threaten and maintain self-esteem. First, it is clear that self-esteem does not change simply on the basis of normative influence and therefore is not something transmitted by association with individuals of higher self-worth. Instead, the person must actively engage in favorable social comparison processes and receive feedback regarding the bases for his or her successes and failures in interacting with the environment. If the person receives continuously negative or ambiguous feedback, favorable comparison processes are unlikely to occur, and lower self-esteem might be expected. Groups that are stigmatized, including persons with disabilities, appear lower in self-esteem because of these processes. Despite possible efforts at self-esteem maintenance, people who are exposed to threats to self-esteem of long duration appear especially vulnerable. Applied studies describing the important causal variables have led to fruitful intervention strategies as well as grater conceptual clarity regarding the process of self-esteem change (Lindzey & Aronson, 1985). (*See also:* Body Image Theory; Secondary Gain; Self-Concept.)

References/Recommended Readings

Lindzey, G., & Aronson, E. *Handbook of social psychology* (3rd ed.). New York: Random House.

Maddox, G. L. (Ed.). (1987). *The encyclopedia of aging.* New York: Springer Publishing Co.

Newman, B. M., & Newman, P. R. (1987). *Development through life: A psychosocial approach* (4th ed.). Chicago: Dorsey Press.

Wylie, R. C., Miller, P. J., Cowles, S. S., & Wilson A. W. (1979). *The self-concept* (vol. II). Lincoln: University of Nebraska Press.

SELF-HELP GROUPS. Groups composed of persons who want to cope with a specific problem or life crisis that meet for the purpose of exchanging information, providing social support, discussing mutual problems, and improving psychological functioning. *Usage Notes and Comments:* Characterized by homogeneity and cohesion, group members have a relatively well-defined, common problem and/or share a common life experience. Powell (1987) organized a typology of self-help groups by their basic mission: (1) habit disturbance organizations emphasize specific behavioral change (e.g., Alcoholics Anonymous, Gamblers' Anonymous); (2) general purpose organizations address a range of difficulties such as dealing with the death of a child (Compassionate Friends), child abuse and neglect (Parents Anonymous), helping persons who had been in mental health facilities (Recovery, Inc.); (3) lifestyle organizations support individuals who are outside mainstream society, experience social isolation, and are often targets of discrimination, such as men and women who are homosexual (National Gay and Lesbian Task Force), the elderly (Gray Panthers), and single parents (Parents Without Partners); (4) significant other organizations provide advocacy, education, support and partnership for relatives of individuals with disabilities (e.g., National Alliance for the Mentally Ill, Al-Anon); and (5) physical handicap organizations that support individuals with distress or disorders like epilepsy (Epilepsy Foundation) or cerebral palsy (Cerebral Palsy Association).

Self-help groups are usually free to the consumer, largely member governed with reliance on fellow members as the primary caregivers, and generally focused on experiential wisdom rather than technical expertise. Professional roles are usually limited to consultation. For these reasons, self-help groups are an important community resource that can be used either in lieu of professional help or as an adjunct. Although rigorous outcome studies of the effectiveness of self-help groups are sparse and findings of those that have been conducted are inconsistent (Levy, 1984), it is thought that those who actively participate on a long-term basis show moderate improvement in functioning, whereas members who are passive find less benefit (Powell, 1987). (*See also:* Independent Living.)

References/Recommended Readings

Jacobs, M. K., & Goodman, G. (1989). Psychology and self-help groups: Predictions on a partnership. *American Psychologist, 44,* 536–545.

Kanfer, F. H., & Goldstein, A. P. (1991). *Helping people change: A textbook of methods* (4th ed.). Elmsford, NY: Pergamon Press.

Kaplan, H. I., & Sadock, B. J. (Eds.). (1991). *Comprehensive glossary of psychiatry and psychology.* Baltimore: Williams & Wilkins.

Levy, L. H. (1984). Issues in research and evaluation. In A. Gartner & F. Riessman (Eds.), *The self-help revolution* (pp. 155–172). New York: Human Sciences Press.

Powell, T. J. (1987). *Self-help organizations and professional practice.* Silver Spring, MD: National Association of Social Workers.

Prochaska, J. D., & Norcross, J. C. (1982). The future of psychotherapy: A Delphi poll. *Professional Psychology, 13,* 620–627.

SICK ROLE BEHAVIOR   Any activity undertaken by
persons who consider themselves sick for the purpose of getting
well. *Usage Notes and Comments:* Receiving treatment from
appropriate professionals and assuming a dependent role are the
principal activities of the sick role. (*See also:* Acceptance of
Disability.)

Recommended Reading

Dimond, M., & Jones, S. (1983). *Chronic illness across the life
span.* Norwalk, CN: Appleton-Century-Crofts.
Parsons T. (1958). Definitions of health and illness in light of
American values and social structures. In E. C. Jaco (Ed.),
*Patients, physicians, and illness: Sourcebook in behavioral
science and medicine* (pp. 165–187). Glencoe, IL: Free Press.

SOCIAL ROLE THEORY.   A theory that holds as one
of its central constructs the notion of status, which is defined as
a collection of rights and duties. *Usage Notes and Comments:* A
role represents the dynamic aspect of a status in which individuals put the rights and duties that constitute a particular
status into effect. Roles and statuses are interdependent with
there being no statuses without roles or roles without statuses.
In the case of disability, it is hypothesized that persons primarily enact roles according to their expectations, or role set, for and
about the so-called "sick role" (English, 1977). (*See also:* Acceptance of Disability.)

References/Recommended Readings

Davis, K. (1949). *Human society.* New York: MacMillan.
English, R. W. (1977). The application of personality theory to
explain psychological reactions to physical disability (pp.
90–129). In R. P. Marinelli & A. E. Dell Orto (Eds.), *The
psychological and social aspects of physical disability.* New
York: Springer Publishing Co.
Gordon, G. (1966). *Role theory and illness.* New Haven, CT:
College and University Press Services, Inc.
Linton, R. (1936). *The study of man.* New York: Appleton-
Century-Crofts.

Parsons, T. (1951). *The social system*. Glencoe, IL: The Free Press.

SOMATOPSYCHOLOGY. The study of the impact of physical disability and chronic illness on personality and interpersonal behavior. *Usage Notes and Comments:* The concept of somatopsychology (referred to by some as interpersonal theory) was initially developed by Barker, Wright, and Gonick (1946) and elaborated by Dembo, Leviton, and Wright (1956), Wright (1960; 1983), and Shontz (1975). Somatopsychology is both a field of scientific study and a compendium of clinical principles regarding the process of adjustment to physical disability. (*See also:* Acceptance of Disability; Developmental Stage Model; Enlarging the Scope of Values; Expectation Discrepancy; Insider vs. Outsider Phenomenon; Interpersonal Theory; Just World Hypothesis; Mourning, Requirement of; Overlapping Situations.)

References

Barker, R. G., Wright, B. A., & Gonick, M. R. (1946). *Adjustment to physical handicap and illness: A survey of the social psychology of physique and disability* (Bulletin 55). New York: Social Science Research Council.

Dembo, T., Leviton, G. L., & Wright, B. A. (1956). Adjustment to misfortune: A problem of social-psychology rehabilitation. *Artificial limbs, 3*(2), 4–62. (Reprinted in *Rehabilitation Psychology*, 1975, *22*, 1–100.)

Shontz, F. C. (1973). *The psychological aspects of physical illness and disability*. New York: Macmillan.

Wright, B. A. (1960). *Physical disability—A psychological approach*. New York: Harper & Row.

Wright, B. A. (1983). *Physical disability—A psychosocial approach* (2nd ed). New York: Harper & Row.

SPREAD. A term, introduced by Dembo, Leviton, and Wright (1956) referring to the tendency to overgeneralize the effects of disability as limiting a person in functions that are actually unrelated to the disability. *Usage Notes and Comments:*

The concept of spread is used to explain how people generalize from a single characteristic, such as crippling, to a vast array of expectations concerning personality and behavior. In a study conducted by Mussen and Barker (1944), students were asked to rate "cripples" in general on 24 personality traits with the finding that publicly expressed attitudes toward persons with physical disabilities are, for the most part, favorable and frequently positive. In a second experiment (Ray, 1946), high-school students were shown several photographs of college men to be ranked according to a number of behaviors and personality characteristics. A photograph of a man sitting in a wheelchair was presented to half the subjects; the same picture with the wheelchair blocked out was shown to the remaining subjects. When depicted as being in a wheelchair or compared to being able-bodied, the stimulus person was judged to be more conscientious, a better friend, to get better grades, to be more even-tempered, to like parties less, and to be more unhappy. (*See also:* Expectation Discrepancy; Interpersonal Theory; Normalization Principle; Stigma).

References

Dembo, T., Leviton, G. L., & Wright, B. A. (1956). Adjustment to misfortune: A problem of social-psychological rehabilitation. *Artificial limbs, 3*(2), 4–62. (Reprinted in *Rehabilitation Psychology,* 1975, *22,* 1–100.)

Mussen, P. H., & Barker, R. G. (1944). Attitudes toward cripples. *Journal of Abnormal Psychology, 39,* 351–355.

Ray, H. M. (1946). *The effect of crippling appearance on personality judgment.* Master's thesis, Stanford University.

Wright, B. A. (1983). *Physical disability—A psychosocial approach.* New York: Harper & Row.

STIGMA. Distinguishing an attribute or quality of a person in such a way that it discredits or minimizes the contributions of that person or marks the person as less useful with the accompanying perceptions and beliefs culminating in a global perception of deviance that is subsequently labeled in some fashion. *Usage Notes and Comments:* The concept of stigma is commonly used to describe persons who possess a physical, psychological, or other characteristic that differs from the perceived norm with that characteristic being readily apparent to those in the majority group. Once the stigma is identified, majority group members generally assume that the person is deviant and socially disadvantaged.

Stigma is often described as a catalyst for a variety of interpersonal and social behaviors as people attempt to "manage" the deleterious effects of the stigma. Resulting behaviors could be in the form of gratuitous displays of kindness, attempts to hide or disguise the stigma, or in efforts to aid those believed to be disadvantaged by the stigma. Primarily, stigma is believed to be grounded in biological differences, and the contribution of culture, society, environment, and context in defining the condition as stigma is ignored. (*See also:* Devaluation; Normalization Principle; Positivity [Sympathy] Bias.)

Recommended Readings

Fine, M., & Asch, A. (1988). Disability beyond stigma: Social interaction, discrimination, and activism. *Journal of Social Issues, 44,* 3–21.

Goffman, E. (1963). *Stigma: Notes on management of spoiled identity.* Englewood Cliffs, NJ: Prentice-Hall.

Jones, E. E., Farina, A., Hastorf, A. H., Markus, H., Miller, D. T., & Scott, R. (1981). *Social stigma: The psychology of marked relationships.* New York: W. H. Freeman & Co.

Katz, I. (1981). *Stigma: A social psychological analysis.* Hillsdale, NJ: Lawrence Erlbaum.

Wright, B. A. (1983). *Physical disability—A psychosocial approach.* New York: Harper & Row.

STRESS MANAGEMENT. A technique by which one attempts to manage the cognitive, behavioral, affective, and physiological components of stress. *Usage Notes and Comments:* Stress is experienced when environmental demands tax or exceed the physiological, personal, or social resources of an individual. Individual reactions to the stresses of a disability are dependent on several factors, such as acknowledgment of disability and goal setting (Roessler, 1988), understanding of the disability and its treatment (Falloon, 1988), economic strains and feelings of stigma (Leyser & Dekel, 1991), and the severity, chronicity, and specific characteristics of the disability (Cherry, 1989). Chronic or acute stress can lead to gastrointestinal, cardiovascular, respiratory, musculoskeletal, and skin disorders as well as psychological and immunological manifestations (Everly & Rosenfeld, 1981).

Techniques for manging stress often focus on changing cognitive appraisal processes by: (1) realizing one's self-responsibility—the person with a disability is an active participant with the clinician and family members in the treatment intervention (Everly & Rosenfeld, 1981), (2) "reframing" or viewing problems from different perspectives, possibly resulting in different solutions or a re-definition of stressful events (Cameron, Armstrong-Stassen, Orr, & Loukas, 1991), and (3) assessing one's strengths and needs, possibly leading to a better understanding of one's actions and reactions (Farmer, Monahan, & Hekeler, 1984).

Relaxation techniques have also proven useful in the treatment of excessive stress and its clinical syndromes. The most commonly used techniques include progressive relaxation (reducing the neural activity and contractile tension in striate skeletal muscles through a series of muscular contractions), meditation (inducing a relaxed state through the utilization of a repetitive focal device such as one's breathing or counting), controlled breathing (voluntarily altering one's rhythmic pattern of breathing to create a more relaxed state), and various forms of biofeedback (collecting and processing data regarding one's biological activity).

Finally, external or physical agents can help in coping with stressful conditions. Dietary recommendations to increase nutritional status as well as physical exercise to improve muscle tone and cardiovascular strength may be important contributors to a sense of health and well-being. In certain cases, a pharmacological approach, including sedatives or antianxiety agents, can be beneficial, although the danger for dependency and abuse may be a consideration before its use.

References/Recommended Readings

Cameron, S., Armstrong-Stassen, M., Orr, R., & Loukas, A. (1991). Stress, coping, and resources in mothers of adults with developmental disabilities. *Counseling Psychology, 4,* 301–310.

Cherry, D. (1989). Stress and coping in families with ill or disabled children: Application of a model to pediatric therapy. *Physical and Occupational Therapy Pediatrics, 9,* 11–32.

Everly, G., & Rosenfeld, R. (1981). *The nature and treatment of the stress response: A practical guide for clinicians.* New York: Plenum Press.

Falloon, I. (1988). Behavioral family management in coping with functional psychosis: Principles, practice, and recent developments. *International Journal of Mental Health, 17,* 35–47.

Farmer, R., Monahan, L., & Hekeler, R. (1984). *Stress management for human services.* Beverly Hills: Sage Publications.

Leyser, Y., & Dekel, G. (1991). Perceived stress and adjustment in religious Jewish families with a child who is disabled. *Journal of Psychology, 125,* 427–438.

Meichenbaum, D. (1985). *Stress innoculation training.* New York: Pergamon.

Roessler, R. (1988). A conceptual basis for return to work interventions. *Rehabilitation Counseling Bulletin, 32,* 98–107.

STRUCTURED EXPERIENTIAL THERAPY (SET-R).

A form of group therapy described by Dell Orto and colleagues (1975, 1977) in which persons with physical disabilities and the able-bodied meet together to share growth experiences and to develop social skills. *Usage Notes and Comments:* The rationale for using group process in a SET-R format was to introduce the dimensions of goal orientation, accountability, mutuality, and skill generalization into group therapy for rehabilitation populations.

References

Dell Orto, A. E. (1975). Goal group therapy: A structured group experience applied to drug treatment and rehabilitation. *Journal of Psychedelic Drugs, 7,* 363–371.

Lasky, R. G., Dell Orto, A. E., & Marinelli, R. P. (1977). Structured experiential therapy: A group approach to rehabilitation (pp. 319–341). In R. P. Marinelli & A. E. Dell Orto (Eds.), *The psychological and social impact of physical disability.* New York: Springer Publishing Co.

SUCCUMBING FRAMEWORK. *See* Coping Versus Succumbing Frameworks.

SYMPATHY BIAS. *See* Positivity Bias.

TRAIT-AND-FACTOR APPROACH. An approach
to counseling, particularly career counseling, in which career
decisions, goals, and plans are facilitated through systematic,
rational, cognitively-oriented, problem-solving methods, emphasizing development of self-knowledge on the part of the individual serving in relation to occupations and corresponding
work environments. *Usage Notes and Comments:* The classical
trait-and-factor approach is based on the work of Williamson
and his associates (Williamson, 1939, 1950, 1972) and is characterized by empirically based methods deriving in large part
from differential psychology, particularly testing and assessment, in matching individuals to work environments consistent
with their characteristics. Williamson described the approach as
being comprised of six steps: analysis, synthesis, diagnosis,
prognosis, counseling, and follow-up.

Contemporary trait-and-factor approaches have been referred
to as the person-environment (P x E) approach to counseling
(Chartrand, 1991; Kosciulek, 1993; Rounds and Tracy, 1990).
The P x E approach is characterized as dynamic, process-
oriented, and accounting for the complex, reciprocal interactions
occurring between person and environment in contrast to the
more static matching of individuals to occupations, which characterized the classical trait-and-factor approach. In addition, a
broader view is now proposed in conceptualizing work environments, including such characteristics as ability requirements,
social climate, physical characteristics, rewards provided, and
more sophisticated methods of measuring and assessing such
aspects of work environments have also been developed.

References/Recommended Readings

Brown, D. (1990). Trait and factor theory. In D. Brown, L.
    Brooks, & Associates (Eds.), *Career choice and development*
    (pp. 13–36). San Francisco: Jossey-Bass.
Chartrand, J. M. (1991). The evolution of trait-and-factor
    career counseling: a person x environment fit approach.
    Journal of Counseling and Development, 69, 518–524.

Kosciulek, J. F. (1993). Advances in trait-and-factor theory: A person x environment fit approach to rehabilitation counseling. *Journal of Applied Rehabilitation Counseling, 24*(2) 11–14.

Rounds, J. B., & Tracey, J. J. (1990). From trait-and-factor to person-environment fit counseling: Theory and process. In W. B. Walsh & S. H. Osipow (Eds.), *Career counseling* (pp. 1–44). Hillsdale, NJ: Erlbaum.

Williamson, E. G. (1939). *How to counsel students: A manual of techniques for clinical counselors.* New York: McGraw-Hill.

Williamson, E. G. (1950). *Counseling adolescents.* New York: McGraw-Hill.

Williamson, E. G. (1972). Trait-and-factor theory and individual differences. In B. Steffire & W. H. Grant (Eds.), *Theories of counseling* (2nd ed., pp. 136–176). New York: McGraw-Hill.

VOCATIONAL REHABILITATION ACT (VRA) OF 1973. An Act that has as its purpose "to develop and implement, through research, training, services, and the guarantee of equal opportunity, comprehensive and coordinated programs of vocational rehabilitation and independent living, for individuals with handicaps in order to maximize their employability, independence, and integration into the work place and the community" (Henry, 1991, p. 124). *Usage Notes and Comments:* The VRA of 1973 approaches its purpose much differently than another more recent major piece of legislation, the Americans with Disabilities Act (ADA) of 1990. The VRA is designed (1) to provide a clear and comprehensive national mandate for the elimination of discrimination against individuals with disabilities; (2) to provide clear, strong, consistent, enforceable standards addressing discrimination against individuals with disabilities; (3) to ensure that the Federal Government plays a central role in enforcing the standards established in this Act on behalf of individuals with disabilities; and (4) to invoke the sweep of congressional authority, including the power to enforce the fourteenth amendment and to regulate commerce, in order to address the major areas of discrimination faced day-to-day by people with disabilities.

One significant difference between the VRA and the ADA is that the VRA does not contain protections for people associating with those who are disabled. Section 102(b)(4) of the ADA extends protection to individuals who are discriminated against because of their relationship or association with an individual with a disability. Although the employer may not discriminate against someone with a sick relative, the employer is not required, under the ADA, to provide reasonable accommodation to that person. (*See also:* Americans with Disabilities Act of 1990; Qualified Handicapped Person; Reasonable Accommodation.)

References/Recommended Readings

Frierson, J. G. (1989). Determining coverage under the handicapped employment laws. *Labor Law Journal, 40*(10), 630–641.

Henry, K. D. (1991). Civil rights and the disabled: A comparison of the Rehabilitation Act of 1973 and the Americans with Disabilities Act of 1990 in the employment setting. *Albany Law Review, 54*(1), 123–140.

Mahoney, R. E., & Gibofsky, A. (1992). The Americans with Disabilities Act of 1990. *Journal of Legal Medicine, 13*, 51–75.

Maffeo, P. A. (1990). Making non-discriminatory fitness-for-duty decisions about persons with disabilities under the Rehabilitation Act and the Americans with Disabilities Act. *American Journal of Law & Medicine, 16*(3), 179–326.

Tucker, B. P. (1989). Section 504 of the Rehabilitation Act after ten years of enforcement: The past and the future. *University of Illinois Law Review, Fall*(4), 845–921.

Wright, G. N. (1980). *Total rehabilitation.* Boston: Little, Brown and Co.

WORK DISABILITY.
A health problem or disability that prevents persons from working or that limits the kind or amount of work they can perform. *Usage Notes and Comments:* Passage of the Americans with Disability Act (ADA) has focused increased attention on the issue of work disability. ADA's provisions for reasonable accommodation and safeguards to limit discrimination against persons with disabilities, already required of federal funds recipients, now extends to virtually all employers. The scope of the ADA is not limited to the work

place, given the components of the law addressing access by persons with disabilities to a range of services provided to the public by either governmental or private entities. Clearly, however, the employment implications of the law are profound, highlighting work disability as an important issue.

Several national surveys collect data on the prevalence of work disability. One recent source is the Current Population Survey conducted by the Census Bureau in 1988. Specifically, the Census Bureau classified persons as having a work disability if they met any of the following criteria: (1) a health problem or disability that prevents them from working or that limits the kind or amount of work they can do; (2) a service-connected disability or ever having retired or left a job for health reasons; (3) a long-term physical or mental illness or disability that prevents the performance of any kind of work; (4) unemployment during the previous year because of illness or disability; (5) under 65 years of age and covered by Medicare; or (6) under 65 years of age and a recipient of Supplemental Security Income (SSI) (National Institute on Disability and Rehabilitation Research, 1992).

The Census Bureau further classified a person as having a severe work disability if any of items 3 through 6 applied. Using these criteria, the Census Bureau estimates that 8.6% of the population (13.4 million persons) 16 to 64 years of age had a work disability in 1988, of which 7.5 million or 4.8% had a severe work disability. The rates of work disability and severe work disability for males were 8.7% and 4.9%, whereas for females they were 8.4% and 4.6%, respectively. Implicit in this severity ranking is a third classification for those with a nonsevere work disability with a rate of 3.8% for both males and females (National Institute on Disability and Rehabilitation Research, 1992). (*See also:* Activity Limitation; Disability; Functional Limitation.)

References

National Institute on Disability and Rehabilitation Research. (1992). *Digest of data on persons with disabilities*. Washington, DC: U.S. Department of Education.

WORK HARDENING. A physical rehabilitation program that uses graded work tasks to progressively increase the bodily strength, mobility, flexibility, and endurance necessary to return to work. *Usage Notes and Comments:* Sometimes referred to as a "functional industrial rehabilitation program," the work hardening strategy was developed to enable employees injured in industrial accidents to return to work as soon as possible. The focus of work hardening is the physical conditioning of biomechanical, neuromuscular, and cardiovascular functions through progressively more demanding simulated job activities. Work hardening programs begin with a comprehensive functional capacities evaluation to establish current physical performance levels. A work-oriented physical rehabilitation strategy drawing on the disciplines of physical therapy, occupational therapy, and vocational evaluation, the individualized work hardening program typically requires between three and ten weeks of full-time participation. (*See also:* Functional Assessment; Functional Limitation.)

Recommended Reading

Matheson, L. (1984). *Work capacity evaluation: An interdisciplinary approach to industrial rehabilitation.* Anaheim, CA: Employment and Rehabilitation Institute of California.

EPILOGUE

Professional–Client Communication in Rehabilitation Practice: Review and Research Agenda*

Robert L. Glueckauf

As Dr. Eisenberg suggested in the *Preface* of the current text, confusion about the meaning of words used commonly in rehabilitation has been a major stumbling block for effective communication between helping professionals and clients with disabilities. Common terms, such as acceptance of disability and handicap, may have "one meaning for persons unfamiliar with psychosocial rehabilitation concepts" and another for professionals "schooled in rehabilitation theory and practice" (p. ix).

It is important, however, to recognize that semantic difficulties are only one facet of a larger dilemma facing the field of clinical rehabilitation. We currently have only limited knowledge about the communication processes we routinely use to convey information to clients and to guide rehabilitation practice. We possess even less understanding about how communication between clients with disabilities and family members in common rehabilitation situations (e.g., family conferences) affects the behavior and attitudes of rehabilitation professionals.

Why is it that such crucial issues are so poorly understood? What do we actually know about the factors influencing pro-

*The author gratefully acknowledges the comments and suggestions of Gary R. Bond, Alexandra L. Quittner, and Beatrice A. Wright on earlier drafts of this chapter.

fessional–client communication and intervention outcome? What are the implications of research on professional–client communications for the field of rehabilitation? The overall purpose of this chapter is to draw attention to these issues, particularly the need for theory and empirical research on the role of communication in rehabilitation practice.

The plan of the chapter is as follows: (a) to briefly summarize the rehabilitation literature focusing on the role of communication, particularly devaluing language in shaping attitudes and behavior toward persons with disabilities, (b) to briefly review the pertinent research on physician–patient communication and health outcome, and (c) to propose future directions for research on the role of communication in rehabilitation practice.

OBSERVATIONS ON COMMUNICATION IN REHABILITATION PSYCHOLOGY

Concern about the impact of professional–client communication in rehabilitation can be traced to the early theorizing of Tamara Dembo, Beatrice Wright, and colleagues on the psychosocial consequences of disability (e.g., Dembo, 1964; Dembo, Leviton, & Wright, 1956/1975; Wright, 1960, 1983, 1987). These authors have emphasized the importance of professional–client communication in either fostering self-respect or reinforcing so-called "sick role" behavior (Parsons, 1958). Wright (1987), for example, asserted that the common hospital practice of calling persons with disabilities "quads, hips, or back cases" violates the "basic precepts of human dignity" and diminishes the individual's social status from "personhood," to "object" in need of treatment and supervision (p. 13).

Surprisingly, there has been no published empirical research that directly assesses the impact of professional–client communication on the outcomes of rehabilitation practice. Most investigators (e.g., Adler, Wright, & Ulicny, 1991; Dooley & Gliner, 1989; Patterson & Witten, 1987) have examined broad-based relationships between language content and attitudes toward persons with disabilities. Furthermore, the majority of these studies have been conducted with undergraduate students and have relied primarily on analogue methodologies.

Adler et al., for example, (1991) examined the effects of fund raising appeals on the attitudes and altruistic behavior of introductory psychology students. The results indicated that students who viewed "video spots" portraying persons with disabilities in favorable terms (e.g., "lives independently," "enjoys sports") expressed significantly more positive attitudes toward persons with disabilities, than subjects who were exposed to devaluing messages (e.g., "parents worry constantly and must check up on him," "takes all his effort to partake in these activities"). No significant differences, however, were found for the amount students were willing to donate. The authors concluded that language content had a substantial impact on subjects' attitudes toward persons with disabilities, but did not change their overt behavior.

Adler et al.'s findings were consistent with the results of earlier studies in this area (e.g., Harris, 1975; Harris & Harris, 1977; Shurka, Siller, & Dvonch, 1982). In general, negative portrayals of persons with disabilities, either through brief, written scenarios or video presentation, perpetuate negative stereotypes, whereas exposure to positive or "coping" representations lead to significantly more positive attitudes toward persons with disabilities.

Although the above studies suggest that the content of oral and written descriptions of persons with disabilities can modify the attitudes of the "receiver," the psychological conditions linking language content, attitude change, and behavioral responding remain poorly understood. Fortunately, there is a more extensive body of research in public health and family medicine to help us identify factors that may influence communication processes between health care providers and clients.

Research on Provider-Patient Communication

Roter, Hall, and Katz (1988) synthesized the findings of 61 studies of physician–patient communication in routine office and hospital interviews. In over 75% of studies, verbal exchanges between physicians and patients were taperecorded and subsequently content analyzed. The majority of these physician–patient interactions were first visits. The patients were predominantly adults, women, racially heterogeneous, and from low or middle economic strata. Although patients' medical conditions were not specifically described, the primary diagnoses consisted of a mix of "acute and chronic medical conditions" (p. 104).

Using a modified Q-sort procedure, Roter et al. classified 247 provider and patient process variables from the 61 communication studies into six broad categories: (1) information giving, (2) information seeking, (3) partnership building, (4) social conversation, (5) positive talk, and (6) negative talk. Approximately 55% of patient verbalizations were efforts at information giving; 20% was positive talk, and the remaining 20% was equally divided among social conversation (7%), question asking (6%), and negative talk (7%). Information seeking (i.e., asking questions to gain information and clarification) was found to be more common for physicians than for patients, accounting for 23% of physician interaction. Similar to patients, however, information giving was the most common physician behavior (39%); the remainder included positive talk (15%), partnership building (10%), social conversations (5%), and negative talk (1%).[1]

Two characteristics of physician–patient interaction, proportion of time spent in negative talk and in partnership building, were particularly noteworthy. Only 1% of physicians' verbalizations was comprised of negative talk (i.e., talk with a negative tone or affect) as compared to 7% for patient behavior. The authors did not address the reasons for the low occurrence of negative talk. It seems plausible, however, that situational factors, such as the time pressures of routine office practice and early physician training experiences (i.e., instruction and modeling in avoiding direct conflict with patients), may have been important influences.

"Partnership-building" statements (i.e., physicians' efforts to gain greater patient input, and to interpret and synthesize patients' comments) accounted for approximately 10% of physician talk. Interestingly, the authors hypothesized that partnership-building efforts may signal either more "egalitarian exchange, or, paradoxically, . . . problematic encounters in which patients appear withdrawn, reticent, or uncomprehending" (p. 109). They emphasized that further research is needed to determine whether negative or positive interactions account for most of the variation in physician partnership-building efforts.

Roter et al. (1988) also examined several relationships be-

---

[1]Percentages of the total patient and physician verbalizations are median approximations and do not sum to 100%.

tween demographic and setting factors, and physician–patient communication. Physicians provided significantly more medical information, engaged in higher levels of positive talk and asked fewer questions of white than of Hispanic or black patients. Physicians also spent more time in positive talk with new patients than those who were returning for follow-up. Medical setting was found to exert a significant influence on physician–patient interaction. Doctors spent twice as much time with patients seen in the hospital, as compared to those seen in private practice. They also asked fewer questions, while spending more time in partnership-building interactions with hospital patients, compared to private patients. Finally, length of visit was significantly correlated with years of medical practice. Experienced physicians had shorter visits with patients than physicians in training.

The degree to which physician–patient relationships parallel relationships between rehabilitation professionals and clients is unknown. However, the literature on the former at least offers a methodological and theoretical "starting point." Investigators can draw on this research to design descriptive studies of communication patterns between staff members and clients. The first step would be to carefully document the frequency and types of social exchanges across different rehabilitation activities, contexts, and professional specialties. If our ultimate objective, however, is to assess the effects of professional–client communication on rehabilitation outcome, we must go beyond simple descriptive studies of professional–client interaction and design experimental investigations.

Over the past decade, medical education researchers have begun to examine the causal linkages between doctor–patient communication and patient health outcomes. Most of our knowledge about this subject comes from studies evaluating the effects of communication training on the interviewing skills of medical professionals and patients.

In their recent comprehensive review, Anderson and Sharpe (1991) divided communication training studies into two major categories: provider-targeted and patient-targeted interventions. Seventy-five percent of studies ($n = 30$) focused on health care providers, such as medical students, hospital interns and residents, community-based physicians, nurse practitioners, and physician's assistants, and the remaining 25% focused on patient training.

Provider-targeted interventions typically consisted of interview skills training using a combination of didactic instruction, modeling, and feedback. Length of training varied between 1.5 and 4 hours. Note that most studies ($n = 19$) evaluated providers' interview skills in interactions with patient actors, who were trained to play the role of the patient. In seven of these studies, simulated patients also served as trainers and provided systematic feedback on providers' interviewing performance.

The most consistent pattern of results for provider communication training was found for medical student students. Medical students who received interview skills training showed significantly greater skill in interview organization, questioning, rapport, transitional statements, and documentation of data than students who participated in placebo discussion groups or received no training. However, there was considerable variation in outcomes among more experienced health care providers, including community-based physicians, residents/interns, physician's assistants and nurse practitioners. Approximately 50% of the outcome studies on nonstudent practitioner samples found little or no effect for training. Anderson and Sharpe attributed this inconsistency to the wide variation in outcome variables and training methods used across these disparate provider groups. This variability contrasted with the relatively high homogeneity of measures and methods used in the medical student studies.

The goals of patient-targeted communication programs were more circumscribed than provided-targeted interventions. Patients received either (a) verbal prompts or written messages to ask more questions, or (b) more comprehensive instruction in decision making in which "question-asking" skills were embedded. Training typically involved a single, 10- to 20-minute session delivered prior to the doctor's visit.

The overall results of patient-targeted intervention studies were positive with decision-making interventions showing the largest effect size values. Experimental group patients made significantly greater gains in the number of questions asked and comments posed during doctors' visits than subjects in the placebo or no-treatment control conditions. Particularly noteworthy, patients who received the more comprehensive decision-making programs not only exhibited posttreatment gains in question-asking and information-seeking skills, but also showed increased perceptions of overall health, greater preference for taking an active role in treatment, and concomitant decreases in health concerns, and worries about physical and role limitations imposed by their medical conditions; as compared to control subjects. The findings of the latter studies are especially important because they represent an initial effort in assessing the linkages between communication skills enhancement and patient health outcomes.

Future Research on Communication in Rehabilitation Settings

Four specific directions for research on professional–client communication in rehabilitation settings are proposed: (1) descriptive studies on factors contributing to the efficacy and utility of professional–client communication, (2) studies examining the linkages between professional–client communication and client health outcomes, (3) research on the role of family involvement in professional–client communication, and (4) research on the effects of nonhandicapping language.

Descriptive Studies. As noted previously, there have been no published studies describing the types, locations, and frequency of treatment-related communications between staff and clients in rehabilitation settings. It is essential that we initiate this important line of research. Without such information we run the risk of failing to assess important, but unanticipated, treatment-related communications, or missing intervention effects as a consequence of sampling in the "wrong places."

It would be wise, however, to consider two caveats before initiating descriptive studies of this nature. First, the scope of the research question needs to be confined to specific client populations, types of professionals, activities, and settings. For example, the therapy routines and professional staff on most stroke units are likely to be different than those in pediatric oncology centers. Mixing data across disparate rehabilitation contexts and populations would yield a noncategorical or summary index of communication factors. Of course, such an index would have limited utility in guiding future communication studies with specific disability groups, age ranges, and rehabilitation professionals (cf., Quittner, Glueckauf, & Jackson, 1990).

The second caveat focuses on the perspective or viewpoint of the subject. As Dembo (1970) has argued, evaluations of the quality and effectiveness of communication may vary as a function of the observer's viewpoint. The client with a disability, family members, and rehabilitation professionals may observe the same interpersonal events, but have very different interpretations of their content and meaning. Thus, descriptive investigations should ideally measure perceptions of quality and utility of professional–client communication from multiple perspective (e.g., client, family members, and rehabilitation professional).

Another important issue in identifying factors that contribute to the efficacy and utility of professional-client communication is choice of methodology. Two methodologies may be particularly well-suited for use in a wide range of rehabilitation contexts: (1) diary recordings, and (2) in-depth interviews.

First, diary methodologies have been used successfully in a variety of studies to measure the frequency, diversity, and locations of activities of persons with disabilities both in rehabilitation facilities and in the community (e.g., Brown & Gordon, 1987; Glueckauf & Quittner, 1992; Quittner, Opipari, Regoli, Jacobsen, & Eigen, 1992). Subjects with disabilities and/or family members are typically asked to fill out a log or checklist indicating where, when, with whom, and what types of activities were performed during the course of the day. Two diary methods, the Self-Observation Report Technique (SORT; Stephens, Norris-Baker, & Willems, 1984) and the Activity Pattern Indicators (API; Diller, Fordyce, Jacobs, & Brown, 1981) may be especially promising because they have shown good psychometric properties across several rehabilitation populations and can be easily adapted to assess significant communication events between professionals and clients. Either approach can be used with minor modifications to examine relationships between specific professional-client interactions (e.g., conversations with physical therapists and medical doctors) and rehabilitation outcomes (e.g., shorter rehabilitation stay, absence from treatment, physical complaints).

Second, retrospective in-depth interviews (IDI), a method adapted from participant observation research (see Jorgensen,

1989), can be used to assess clients' and family members' perceptions of interpersonal events that had either positive or negative effects on rehabilitation outcomes. The major advantages of IDIs are their ease and convenience of administration. Similar to other retrospective methods, however, IDIs may be susceptible to validity threats, such as recall and hindsight errors, as well as experimenter bias.

In-depth interviewing consists primarily of open-ended questions about key interactions between rehabilitation professionals, clients, and family members [e.g., Were there any discussions or experiences you (e.g., the client) had with staff (e.g., social worker, nurses) that had either a positive or negative impact on your rehabilitation program?]. After identifying several "key events", respondents are asked to describe in detail where, when, with whom and what was said or done before, and after the target situation. Last, the client or family member is encouraged to discuss the perceived consequences of each "target" event.

As suggested above, the primary purpose of IDI is heuristic, that is, to identify key professional-client interactions that may have an impact on rehabilitation outcome. It cannot be used as a substitute for more rigorous, longitudinal data collection methods (e.g., daily diaries). Without adequate psychometric support, the validity of relationships between specific communication patterns and health outcomes based on IDI should be considered suspect. Nonetheless, in-depth interviews may provide preliminary guidance in identifying professional-client interactions that have an impact on rehabilitation outcome.

Studies Linking Professional-Client Communication and Rehabilitation Outcomes. Although research on doctor–patient communication (Anderson & Sharpe, 1991) has found an overall positive association between improvements in doctor–patient relations and patient health outcomes, the specific social-psychological mechanisms linking these factors remain poorly understood. Fortunately, rehabilitation settings permit a close examination of the relationships among health care messages, psychosocial functioning, and health outcomes. Most clients adhere to a highly organized schedule of activities, involving daily appointments with therapists, nurses, and other health care professionals. Furthermore, it is routine practice in most rehabilitation facilities to conduct treatment-planning conferences either with the client alone, or with the client and family members.

A major benefit of this structure is the ability to perform evaluations of the impact of professional-client exchanges shortly after they occur, for example, during evening hours when most rehabilitation clients have "time off." Changes in emotional and/or physical functioning (e.g., increased optimism about one's abilities, fewer pain complaints) can also be easily assessed, particularly if embedded within the regular evening medication or vital signs routine. The differential probability of specific contingencies between communication exchanges and client health outcomes can be evaluated using prospective diary methods, such as the SORT or API.

Studies on Family Factors in Professional-Client Communication. One of the most neglected aspects of the study of professional-client communication is the role of family involvement. It is commonplace in most rehabilitation centers for family members to participate in individual and/or group meetings with the client and professional staff at the outset, periodically during the course of treatment, and at the time of discharge.

Although we have no data on the impact of these sessions, it is plausible that clients and family members share their perceptions and feelings about these experiences with one another. In addition, they sometimes voice their opinions about these events to rehabilitation staff members.

As a psychologist and consultant to different medical rehabilitation units, I have received several comments from clients and family members about staff conferences, ranging from "the doctor and the therapists were so good about answering all of our questions" to "the meeting was a big downer; how can the staff tell us that what we see is not real progress?" In my opinion, such planning and evaluation meetings provide a rich source of data on the factors that influence clients' and family members' impressions of the communication skill and emotional sensitivity of rehabilitation professionals. They also may serve as a potential beginning point in examining the linkages among professional-client/family communication, emotional functioning of the client, and rehabilitation outcome.

Of course, clients with disabilities and family members are not the only persons who are affected by planning and evaluation conferences. Rehabilitation professionals are likely to form impressions about the abilities and personality traits of clients and family members, and respond emotionally when confronted with criticism or praise in these situations. It is possible that such events, especially where strong negative affect is aroused, can influence the quality and duration of rehabilitation treatment. Based on my own experience, clients and family members who overtly question the rules of conduct and/or the philosophy of the center tend to be avoided by staff and may be susceptible to shorter rehabilitation stays.

Research on Handicapping Language It is ironic that the topic of language usage, an issue of central importance to the early proponents of psychosocial rehabilitation (Dembo et al., 1956/ 1975; Wright, 1983), has not captured the attention of rehabilitation investigators and educators. Considering that rehabilitation professionals are genuinely concerned about matters related to the dignity of persons with disabilities, why has there been so little empirical research in this area?

One explanation may be that rehabilitation practitioners do not perceive "language issues" as a high priority in everyday rehabilitation practice. They may feel that clients are more concerned about acquiring skills in activities of daily living than how the therapist communicates about their disability. Furthermore, medical and allied health professionals, such as physiatrists, occupational and physical therapists, may be especially reluctant to address concerns about language usage because they view these issues as outside their domain of expertise.

Another explanation may be that rehabilitation professionals perceive research on the use of nonhandicapping language in practice settings as an infringement of their rights for free expression. They may consider the adoption of guidelines on language usage as "one more regulation to follow," rather than a beneficial tool to enhance their communication skill with clients and families.

How can we overcome these barriers to research on language usage in rehabilitation? We may need to embed studies on the effects of nonhandicapping language within the broader context of communication skills training for professional staff. Learning to be a more "effective communicator" is likely to be perceived as a more desirable educational alternative than instruction on language usage.

This is not to suggest that key language concerns, such as exaggerating disability or labeling people by their disability, should not be addressed. However, they should be the focus of a single class or module linked to a larger communication skills program. Suggested guidelines for the use of nonhandicapping language (Wright, this volume) can be disseminated following a panel discussion consisting of both consumers with disabilities and professional staff. Open discussion of sensitivity to language content should be actively encouraged. The effects of such "nonhandicapping language" modules can be assessed using self-report questionnaires, or possibly, through archival analysis (i.e., examining staff's written reports and progress notes).

It still remains an open question whether the use of nonhandicapping language has a significant impact on client's self-perceptions and/or behavior. We need to empirically determine how and under what conditions language content leads to positive and negative client outcomes. It is possible that the use of nonhandicapping language (e.g., using the term, person with epilepsy, rather than "epileptic") may produce positive effects in one context (e.g., at a get-together with acquaintances), but have little or no impact in others (e.g., conversations with close family members). Studies examining the differential effect of language content across settings, events, and persons on client self-perceptions and behavior are essential to the growth of this research area.

In summary, there is a dire need for research on the impact of professional–client communication in rehabilitation settings. We can no longer tout the benefits of highly valued rehabilitation practices, such as family conferences and progress meetings, without solid empirical evidence for their efficacy. If we are to advance as a responsible helping discipline, we must begin to subject our basic assumptions about "what works" in daily communication with our clients to scientific scrutiny.

REFERENCES

Adler, A. B., Wright, B. A., & Ulicny, G. R. (1991). Fundraising portrayals of people with disabilities: Donations and attitudes. *Rehabilitation Psychology, 36,* 231–340.

Anderson, L. A., & Sharpe, P. A. (1991). Improving patient and provider communication: A synthesis and review of communication interventions. *Patient Education and Counseling, 17,* 99–134.

Brown, M., & Gordon, W. A. (1987). Impact of impairment on activity patterns of children. *Archives of Physical Medicine and Rehabiliation, 68,* 828–832.

Dembo, T. (1964). Sensitivity of one person to another. *Rehabilitation Literature, 25,* 231–235.

Dembo, T. (1970). The utilization of psychological knowledge in rehabiliation. *Welfare Review, 8,* 1–7.

Dembo, T., Leviton, G. L., & Wright, B. A. (1975). Adjustment to misfortune: A problem of social-psychological rehabilitation. *Rehabilitation Psychology, 22,* 1–100. [Reprinted from *Artificial Limbs, 3*(2), 4–62].

Diller, L. Fordyce, W. Jacobs, D., & Brown, M. (1981). *Activity pattern indicators timeline training material.* New York: New York University Medical Center.

Dooley, D. N., & Gliner, J. A. (1989). Perceptions of disability labels: Effect of attitude and stimulus presentation. *Rehabilitation Psychology, 34,* 259–270.

Glueckauf, R. L., & Quittner, A. L. (1992). Assertiveness training for disabled adults in wheelchairs: Self-report, role-play, and activity pattern outcomes. *Journal of Consulting and Clinical Psychology, 60,* 419–425.

Harris, R. M. (1975). *The effect of perspective taking, similarity and dependency on raising funds for persons with disabilities.* Unpublished master's thesis, University of Kansas, Lawrence, KS.

Harris, R. M., & Harris, A. C. (1977). Devaluation of the disabled in fund raising appeals. *Rehabilitation Psychology, 24,* 69–78.

Jorgensen, D. L. *Participant observation: A methodology for human studies.* Newbury Park, CA: Sage.

Parsons, T. (1958). Definitions of health and illness in light of American values and social structure. In E. G. Jaco (Ed.), *Patients, physicians, and illness: Sourcebook in behavioral science and medicine* (pp. 165–187). Glencoe, IL: Free Press.

Patterson, J. B., & Witten, B. J. (1987). Disabling language and attitudes toward persons with disabilities. *Rehabilitation Psychology, 32,* 245–248.

Quittner, A. L., Glueckauf, R. L., & Jackson, D. N. (1990). Chronic parenting stress: Moderating vs. mediating effects of social support. *Journal of Personality and Social Psychology, 59,* 1266–1278.

Quittner, A. L., Opipari, L. C., Regoli, M. J., Jacobsen, J., & Eigen, H. (1992). The impact of caregiving and role strain on family life: Comparisons between mothers of children with cystic fibrosis and matched controls. *Rehabilitation Psychology, 37,* 275–290.

Roter, D. L., Hall, J. A., & Katz, N. R. (1988). Patient-physician communication: A descriptive summary of the literature. *Patient Education and Counseling, 12,* 99–119.

Shurka, E., Siller, J., & Dvonch, P. (1982). Coping behavior and personal responsibility as factors in the perception of disabled persons by the nondisabled. *Rehabilitation Psychology, 27,* 225–233.

Stephens, M., Norris-Baker, C., & Willems, E. (1984). Data quality in self-observation and report of behavior. *Behavioral Assessment, 6,* 237–252.

Wright, B. A. (1960). *Physical disability: A psychological approach.* New York: Harper & Row.

Wright, B. A. (1983). *Physical disability: A psychosocial approach* (2nd ed.). New York: Harper & Row.

Wright, B. A. (1987). Human dignity and professional self-monitoring. *Journal of Applied Rehabilitation Counseling, 18*(4), 12–14.

Wright, B. A. (1994). Nonhandicapping language. In M. G. Eisenberg (Ed.), *Key Words in psychosocial rehabilitation: A guide to contemporary usage* (pp. 69–74). New York: Springer Publishing Co.

⑤ *Springer Publishing Company*

SPINAL CORD INJURY, 2nd Edition
An Illustrated Guide for Health Professionals

Marcia Hanak, BSN, MA, CRRN, and
Anne Scott, BSN

This thoroughly updated and revised new edition offers a multidimensional approach to working with spinal cord-injured individuals in acute care, rehabilitation, and community settings. All aspects of spinal cord management are discussed: psychological, physiological, medical, and therapeutic, with emphasis on the importance of integrating the various components of care. New to this edition is a patient–family teaching overview and listing of Spinal Cord Injury Centers. Illustrated throughout.

Praise for the first Edition
"An excellent summary of the basic concepts that are included in comprehensive spinal cord injury systems. The authors have succeeded in organizing complex treatment modalities into a readable, concise handbook." —Rehabilitation Nursing

"...offers a wealth of knowledge concerning the medical needs of the spinal cord-injured patient."
—American Journal of Occupational Therapy

1993   192pp   0-8261-4172-2   softcover

536 Broadway, New York, NY 10012-3955 • (212) 431-4370 • Fax (212) 941-7842

 **Springer Publishing Company**

JOURNAL

REHABILITATION PSYCHOLOGY

Official Journal of the Division of Rehabilitation Psychology of the American Psychological Association

M.G. Eisenberg, PhD, Editor,
L. Diller, PhD,
W.E. Fordyce, PhD, and
B.A. Wright, PhD, Associate Editors

Rehabilitation Psychology is an interdisciplinary journal addressing psychosocial and behavioral aspects of rehabilitation. In addition to empirical research, contents include clinical practice, rehabilitation theory, and policy issues. Articles appearing in the journal represent a wide variety of perspectives and practice settings, with topics that relate to the experience of chronic illness and disability throughout the lifespan.

(4 annual issues) • ISSN 0090-5550

536 Broadway, New York, NY 10012-3955 • (212) 431-4370 • Fax (212) 941-7842

§P *Springer Publishing Company*

REHABILITATION NURSING FOR THE NEUROLOGICAL PATIENT

Marcia Hanak, BSN, MA, CCRN

Here is a practical new reference written especially for practicing nurses who work with neurologically disabled persons. Hanak emphasizes the interrelation of rehabilitation and wellness in this thorough, medical approach to rehabilitation nursing.

Contents:

I. Overview • Wellness Promotion • Patient and Family Education • Neuroanatomy and Physiology Review

II. Nursing Management of Problems Common to Neurorehabilitation • Neurogenic Bladder Management • Neurogenic Bowel Management • Dysphagia Management • Sexuality and Disability

III. Nursing Management of Specific Neurological Disabilities • Traumatic Brain Injury Management • Spinal Cord Injury Management • Cerebral Vascular Accident Management • Multiple Sclerosis Management • Amyotrophic Lateral Sclerosis Management • Parkinson's Disease Management • **Appendixes** • Psychosocial Discharge Planning References • Resource Phone Numbers

240pp   0-8261-7660-7   hardcover

536 Broadway, New York, NY 10012-3955 • (212) 431-4370 • Fax (212) 941-7842

⑤ *Springer Publishing Company*

MEDICAL ASPECTS OF DISABILITY

A Handbook for the Rehabilitation Professional

Myron G. Eisenberg, PhD,
Robert L. Glueckauf, PhD, and
Herbert H. Zaretsky, PhD, Editors

A comprehensive text for students preparing for a career in rehabilitation. Covers the medical aspects of disabling conditions including functional presentation and prognosis. Also serves as an authoritative reference guide for the practitioner.

Partial Contents:

Section I. An Introduction to Key Topics and Issues

BODY SYSTEMS: AN OVERVIEW, *J. H. Ahn*

Section II. Disabling Conditions: Their Functional Presentation, Treatment, Prognosis, and Psychological and Vocational Implications

ACQUIRED IMMUNE DEFICIENCY SYNDROME (AIDS) AND HUMAN IMMUNODEFICIENCY VIRUS (HIV), *R. H. Remien and J. Satriano*

ALZHEIMER'S DISEASE, *B. Reisberg and J. A. Mackell*

CHRONIC PAIN, *D. E. DeGood*

SUBSTANCE ABUSE, *C. C. Saltz and M. Lawton*

1993   432pp   0-8261-7970-3   hardcover

536 Broadway, New York, NY 10012-3955 • (212) 431-4370 • Fax (212) 941-7842